IMAGINATION AND THE GROWTH OF SCIENCE

A. M. Taylor

SCHOCKEN BOOKS · NEW YORK

TO NOEL C. LITTLE

Publishedi n U.S.A. in 1967
by Schocken Books Inc.
67 Park Avenue, New York, N.Y. 10016

FOREWORD

In popular misconception, statements of science are statements of certainties; and scientists are detached and passionless observers, swayed only by experimental evidence. It is the thesis of this book that, on the contrary, philosophy holds science to be incapable of proving anything, and able to say of any hypothesis only that it has not yet been disproved; while history reveals the growth of science as a long story of theories tenaciously held in the face of apparent contradiction, of flights of imagination sustained by little factual evidence, and of brilliant guesses astonishingly forerunning experimental discovery.

The following four chapters were originally lectures, designed to illustrate the aims and methods of physical science, and the changing modes of thought prevailing among physicists. They were delivered at Bowdoin College, Brunswick, Maine, U.S.A., as the Tallman Lectures of 1964–5. The series was founded in 1928 by Frank Gifford Tallman of Wilmington, Delaware, Master of Arts of Bowdoin College, as a memorial to the Bowdoin members of his family. His beneficence has been instumental in bringing to Bowdoin a long line of lecturers, many of them eminent indeed. It is therefore with a sense of humility that I record my pleasure at having been admitted to so distinguished a company, and my thanks to those to whose lot it fell to select me as the lecturer for 1964–5.

A. M. TAYLOR

The University, Southampton
February, 1966

CONTENTS

Chapter 1

EARTH AND SKY

The English poet and mystic, William Blake, said that 'to the eyes of a man of imagination, Nature is imagination itself'; and the New England poet and essayist Ralph Waldo Emerson wrote: 'Science does not know its debt to imagination; Goethe did not believe a great naturalist could exist without this faculty.' In these pages I propose to discuss the role of imagination in the growth of science, to consider some of the current beliefs concerning science and scientists, what science is about and how scientists think, and to contrast these with the facts as I see them.

What is science and what is its purpose? It is not the purpose of science to arrive at a system of absolutely certain, irrevocably true statements. Science is not such a system, and it does not advance towards a state of finality. Science is not identical with what the philosophers call *knowledge*, and it cannot claim to attain truth, nor even probability. But though it can attain neither knowledge nor truth, the striving for understanding is the strongest motive for scientific discovery. Karl Popper said: *All science is cosmology, the problem of understanding the world, ourselves, and our knowledge as part of it.* * So speaks philosophy. I do not think that popular opinion would endorse this view; for popular opinion is apt to confuse science with technological success. As a result of the advances in scientific knowledge in the past 150 years, and particularly in the past fifty years, applied science has made immense developments, especially in the fields of electricity, thermodynamics and aerodynamics. Electrical power, the petrol engine and the aeroplane

* Popper, Karl, *The Logic of Scientific Discovery*. London, Hutchinson, 1958, Preface to the English edition.

1

are some of the results. The successes of technology have transformed our civilization. Many old people living today spent their childhood, even their adolescence, in the latter years of last century; then, the only practicable alternative to steam railway travel was astride a horse, or in a horse-drawn carriage; then, the telephone was a new toy; gas-light had still not ousted the candle and the oil-lamp as the accepted forms of domestic illumination; electric light was an object of admiration for the few, and was yet scarcely contemplated as a likely method of lighting ordinary homes of the future. That world presents such a strange contrast to the life of 1966, that to visualize it needs vigorous exercise of the imagination. Probably many of my readers cannot remember when television was not part of the normal equipment of every home; it would occur to hardly anyone today that not long ago it was necessary to set aside six weeks for a journey to Australia. I am not much more than sixty years old, yet the world even of my childhood – where to see a motor-car in a country lane was an event demanding an excited rush home, to tell incredulous parents of the astonishing sight – would tax the imagination of younger people. Be that as it may, the differences emphasize the stupendous developments of technical and applied science which so short a time has brought to pass. This transformation of our civilization has come so swiftly that our thinking is distorted. The contemporary scene has been so changed by the inventions of applied scientists that the layman forgets that science is a search for understanding of nature, not a striving for power over it, though that may come as a bonus by the way. It is a Holy Grail, not an Aladdin's Lamp that a scientist seeks. The physicist used to be called a natural philosopher; in Scotland the study of physics is still known by its old name of natural philosophy, a salutary reminder of this aspect of science. But knowledge brings power. An abundance of mechanical, electrical and atomic successes of technology has swiftly followed the engineering applications of scientific knowledge, so that it is only natural that, in popular imagination, technological marvels displace the wonders of science; that material results acquire the primacy rightfully accorded to intellectual achievements. The handiwork of the craftsman is mistaken for the intellectual creation of the savant.

There is, however, a more subtle and insidious cause of this misconception. The eyes of the populace have been dazzled by the profusion of technical achievement, but their ears also have been deceived by the very scientists and philosophers themselves. The philosophy of science has been at variance with the practice of scientists. The odd thing is that the scientists have been, for the most part, quite unaware of this. Finding themselves acting in conflict with their accepted theories of knowledge they have, again and again, attempted to remedy this situation either by ignoring the contradiction, or even by promulgating versions which are more fiction than history. Such strange behaviour warrants careful analysis, and I shall examine some of the outstanding examples of the growth of science and the ways in which those concerned have arrived at their discoveries.

Before doing so I will try to sketch the appearance of science and the scientist as I believe it to be seen through the eyes of popular misconception. This is not to set up a straw-man merely for the pleasure of knocking him down. It seems to me that we must be aware of the false qualities in the popular image before we can guard against the danger of believing them to be true; we must be familiar with the errors and their manner of growth, before we can eradicate them; we must see the distortions before we can recognize the true picture.

In popular misconception, science is believed to be omnipotent: what it has not yet achieved it will ultimately achieve. It is believed to be infallible; to say of anything, that it is scientific, is thought to give it the impress of truth, the certainty which brooks no shadow of doubt. Even the packets of breakfast cereals bear witness to this; advertisement owes much of its power to the weight carried by a so-called scientific statement; to attribute scientific qualities to some process or other is to stifle criticism. Naturally, the advertiser allows no hint of uncertainty to mar his claims when he dubs them scientific; hence they become indisputable, eternally true, profoundly significant – at least, they do in the eyes of those susceptible to the wiles of advertising. The television screen and the loudspeaker are as blatant and even more clamorous. Popular journalism preaches the same gospel: science is certainty; the findings of a research team must be true; mistakes are never made; progress is uninterrupted.

A result of this clamour is the unquestioning acceptance of the belief that science has proven such and such statements to be true; that the findings of science correspond to reality, and are therefore inevitable, indisputable and final – claims that no scientist would make, claims that no philosopher could admit. There has been another different influence at work which bolsters this belief. This is the view that even some scientists themselves profess to have of their subject, a view that owes its origin to the immense influence of the philosopher Ernst Mach (1838–1916) who, in 1883, published a book – *Die Mechanik* – in which he developed his conception of science as a convenient summary of experience. The purpose of science, he said, was to save time and trouble in recording observations. Science was the most economical adaptation of thought to facts, and was as external to the facts as is a map, a time-table or a telephone-directory. It must not go beyond experience by affirming anything that cannot be tested by experience; above all, scientists must be prepared immediately to drop a theory the moment an observation turns up to conflict with it. Scientists must have an absolute respect for observations; they must hold scientific theories in judicial detachment. Scientists must be passionless observers, unbiased by emotion, intellectually cold.

The facts are otherwise. The history of science shows us, again and again, great discoveries made by passionate adherence to ideas forged in the white heat of imagination. It shows us slow construction, brick by patient brick, of a scientific edifice, often in complete disregard of apparently conflicting evidence. It shows us bold imaginative leaps made in the dark,

4

in unjustified anticipation of success, only later to receive astonishing experimental confirmation.

The three attributes of commitment, imagination and tenacity seem to be the distinguishing marks of greatness in a scientist. A scientist must be as utterly committed in the pursuit of truth as the most dedicated of mystics; he must be as pertinacious in his struggle to advance into uncharted country as the most indomitable of pioneers; his imagination must be as vivid and ingenious as a poet's or a painter's. Like other men, for success he needs ability and some luck; his imagination may be sterile if he has not a flair for asking the right questions, questions to which nature's reply is intelligible and significant.

But this is to anticipate. Let us first look briefly at the early development of Western Science. Aristotle, who lived from 385 to 325 B.C., invented logic and a deductive system of acquiring knowledge. His writings were collected under the title *To Organon*, that is, the *instrument* by which true knowledge was to be attained. He was saturated in the Greek thought of the period, and this thought was dominated by geometry. It had been found that, starting from clearly stated premisses, a few axioms and definitions, a great interlocking structure of knowledge could be built piece by piece. Such achievement fascinated the Greek geometers, and it was natural for Aristotle to concentrate on the *form* of the argument whatever the subject of discussion. Reasoned argument must, said Aristotle, proceed along a well-defined path. This he called the method of the syllogism, which he defined as 'a discourse in which certain things being stated, something other than what is stated follows of necessity from their being so'.

Aristotle's stimulus to philosophy was immense and fruitful, but his influence on the growth of scientific method was small and detrimental. His tendency to think that knowledge gained by reasoned argument was superior to, almost independent of, knowledge gained directly by observation and experiment, inhibited development of science for twenty centuries. But we should notice that even at his most formal, while his preoccupation with the power of reason led him to analyse the method of the syllogism, he paid tribute also to the intuitive faculties of the mind.

To appreciate this attitude we must pause to consider the nature and purpose of the syllogism. It is a formal statement of two propositions, the premisses, from which a third follows. Aristotle thought science to consist in knowing things through their causes, and the way of demonstrating knowledge could only be by the use of the scientific syllogism. The search for causes reduces to the search for the relevant middle terms of the syllogisms, and this search is prospered by quickness of wit, which is the faculty of hitting upon the essential middle term without delay. This is perhaps the earliest hint that reason plays a subordinate part in scientific practice, that mental agility is of primary importance. The example he gives makes it clear that it is scientific imagination which is needed. The phases of the moon are a matter of common observation, and so are the phenomena of sunshine and shadow. His argument ran:

All things lit by the sun have their bright side sunward;
The moon is lit by the sun;
Therefore the moon has her bright side sunward.

Solving the problem turns on apprehending the truth of the middle term; only because intuition sees that the moon borrows her light from the sun can the conclusion be reached, and the phases of the moon be explained. Without imaginative grasp the problem would remain unsolved.

It may be noted that the example is of the *deductive* method of scientific discovery, in which, starting with a universally true premiss and with a particular premiss, one arrives at a particular conclusion. By the *inductive* method, in contrast to this, one reaches conclusions presumed to be universally valid although developed from particular premisses. To philosophy, induction is always suspect. Aristotle himself defines induction as the attempt to establish a universal on the evidence of groups of particulars to which there is no exception. As our sense-perceptions are of particulars, it appears that philosophy cannot tolerate the scientists' reliance on observation. In spite of this, Aristotle held that the inductive method was valid. He believed that the basic truths of any science are incapable of demonstration, but are only revealed to the soul by intuition. This he called the originative source of scientific knowledge.

Nearly 2,000 years after Aristotle, Francis Bacon (1561–1626) in his great book *Novum Organum* laid down in detail the steps to be taken in pursuing the inductive method. The scientist was to start with observation of a vast number of facts, to proceed to fabricate theories, and to test them by crucial experiments. This is indeed the core of modern scientific method, but all is not so detached and impersonal as Bacon would have us think. The absence of any place in his plan for the making of hypotheses, for the initial leap of the imagination, outrunning observation, jumping far into the unknown – the lack of this is the weakness of his method, is indeed the cause of its failure. Bacon would have us start outwards and work inwards. Modern science starts inwards with an imaginative guess, a reasoned hypothesis, and then works outwards to detailed observation and verification.

In the last century William Whewell (1794–1866), master of Trinity College, Cambridge, classical scholar, mathematician and philosopher, wrote *Novum Organum Renovatum*, in which he contended that *two* processes were essential: first the *colligation of facts*, and then the *explication of conceptions*, and said that 'only the sagacity of discoverers can suggest the appropriate conception'. Such sagacity cannot be taught; it succeeds by guessing. Such success consists in framing several tentative hypotheses and in selecting the right one. But, he says, 'inventive talent is necessary for the supply of appropriate hypotheses.'

A philosopher of our time, Karl Popper of Vienna, now living in England, in his analysis of the problem* concludes that the scientific method consists in first formulating an hypothesis (which must be the result of intuitive guesswork); then

* Popper, Karl, op. cit., pp. 32 and 33.

then deducing logical predictions from the hypothesis; and, finally, fourfold testing in this order:

(a) Comparison of conclusions for internal consistency.
(b) Examination of the logical form of the theory.
(c) Comparison with earlier theories to see if any advance has been made.
(d) Empirical testing of conclusions and predictions.

If predictions are confirmed, the theory is verified; if contradicted, the theory is falsified. So long as theories survive they are said to be corroborated. It is obvious that no theory can ever be *proved* – all that can be said is that it has not so far been *dis*proved. Science can never reach finality. It proceeds step by step in its quest for truth, a will-o'-the-wisp that ever eludes it, always receding, always one step ahead. But always science progresses by making and testing newer, more viable hypotheses. Popper says* of the formulation of these hypotheses:

Science does not rest on rock-bottom. The bold structure of its theories rises as it were above a swamp. It is like a building erected on piles. The piles are driven forward from above the swamp, but not down to any natural base, and when we cease our attempt to drive the piles into a deeper layer it is not because we have reached firm ground. We simply stop when we are satisfied that they are firm enough to carry the structure for the time being. Science does not pursue the illusory aim of making its answers final. Bold imaginative conjectures are required, carefully and soberly controlled by systematic tests. The method of research is not to defend the conjectures to show how right we were, but to try to overthrow them. Using all the weapons of logical, mathematical, and technical armoury, we try to prove our anticipations false, in order to put forward in their stead what Bacon called 'new unjustified anticipations, new rash and premature prejudices'.

This is a *philosopher's* heady rhetoric. But Einstein, the *mathematician*, has said that the supreme task of the physicist

* Popper, Karl, op. cit., p. 111.

8

is to search for universal laws, from which, by pure deduction, a picture of the world may be obtained. There is, he says, 'no logical path leading to these laws. They can be reached only by intuition, and this intuition is based on an intellectual love of the objects of experience'.* This is remarkably similar to Aristotle's view that the basic laws of science can only be revealed to the soul by the faculty of intuition. Einstein admitted that value judgements and personal predilections play a large part in arriving at conclusions; he thought there was an element akin to religious faith in his knowledge of the universe. With this Popper agrees, saying: 'Looking at the matter from the psychological angle, I am inclined to think that scientific discovery is impossible without faith in *ideas*, ideas which are of a purely speculative kind, sometimes even quite *hazy*, a faith completely unwarranted from the point of view of science, and to that extent, metaphysical.'†

Such admissions that value judgements play a vital part in the development and growth of science are by no means restricted to philosophers and mathematicians, but are becoming more and more widely shared by scientists themselves. It is perhaps significant that the turn of the century brought three of the most astonishing, revolutionary and fruitful developments in physics since the seventeenth century. These were the theory of relativity, the quantum theory, and the discovery of radio-activity (which led to nuclear physics). The protagonists were many, but the names most widely recognized, and rightly so, are those of Albert Einstein (1879–1955), Max Planck (1858–1947) and Ernest Rutherford (1871–1937). It is remarkable that many of those who have contributed most to these subjects, especially on the theoretical side, have throughout their lives expressed views the antithesis of those held by men who, with Ernst Mach, judge science to be entirely detached and factual, who believe scientists to be above the storms and turbulence

---

* Einstein, A., Address on the occasion of Max Planck's sixtieth birthday. *Mein Weltbild*, 1934, p. 168; quoted in Popper, op. cit., p. 32.

† Popper, K., op. cit., p. 38.

of human emotions. This conflict of opinions has been recently evaluated by Michael Polanyi, formerly Professor of Physical Chemistry in Manchester University, who in Hungary was a medical practitioner, and who became Professor without a department, free to range over the fields of science and philosophy. He was the Gifford Lecturer in Aberdeen University for 1951–52. He utterly rejects the ideal of scientific detachment.* He says that it is harmless in the exact sciences, for it is there disregarded by the scientists : but that it is a destructive influence in biology, sociology and psychology, and falsifies our outlook far beyond the domain of science. He holds that scientific advance is mediated by passionate commitment of the scientist in his search for rationality in nature. Discoveries are great in so far as they demonstrate this innate rationality. Perhaps not everyone will agree with all his views, but even a brief glance at the lives of scientists supports his assessment of the forces driving them to their achievements.

To illustrate this, consider the work of Copernicus and Kepler. Copernicus lived from 1473 to 1543, and substituted the heliocentric description of the universe for the geocentric one. This was a startling feat. The Ptolemaic system made the earth the central point in the universe. The daily experience of dawn and nightfall, sunrise and sunset, of the firmament of stars wheeling overhead, appealing directly to the senses, made this view of the universe satisfactory to the uncritical observer. Copernicus, in abstraction, took his stand outside the earth, and fixing his imagination in the sun, perceived the ordered motion of the heavenly bodies vastly simplified.

Johann Kepler, who lived from 1571–1630, was attracted to the Copernican hypothesis; but he was steeped in the Pythagorean tradition, which sought the explanation of nature in terms of numbers and especially of geometry. Now there are five, and only five, ways of building a solid figure of regular shape with faces all identical, all similarly inclined to their neigh-

* Polanyi, M., *Personal Knowledge.* University of Chicago Press, Routledge, London, 1958.

bours. The results are: the tetrahedron built from four equilateral triangular faces; the cube with six square faces; the octahedron having eight equilateral triangular faces; the dodecahedron with twelve pentagonal faces, and the icosahedron with twenty equilateral triangular faces. Their number is five and this too is the number of the then known planets of the solar system: Mercury, Venus, Mars, Jupiter and Saturn. The distances of the planets from the sun had long been an object of speculation; at that date there was a mystical element ascribed to numbers themselves, and the ratios of the planetary distances were thought to be of fundamental significance. A man's thoughts are coloured by the temper of the age, so it appeared to Kepler that there must of necessity be a mystical connexion between celestial architecture and the principles of geometry. Five heavenly bodies and five regular geometrical solids! Kepler imagined he had discovered the explanation of the planetary distances in terms of these five regular solids, which, inscribed one inside the other rather in the manner of Chinese boxes, defined the radii of the orbits of the planets. He published this discovery, to which he attached the greatest value, in a book called *Mysterium Cosmographicum* in 1596, which brought him considerable renown. He became assistant to the great Danish astronomer Tycho Brahé (1546–1601), a remarkable observer whose measurements were exact enough for Kepler ultimately to discover from them the famous three laws of planetary motion. The first two of these are that the paths of the planets are ellipses with the sun at one focus, and that the rate of movement is such that the line drawn from the planet to the sun sweeps out equal areas in equal times. These he published in 1609 in his book *Astronomia Nova*, only eight years after he had succeeded, on Tycho Brahé's death, to the post of imperial astronomer to the Emperor Rudolf II. Ten years later, in 1619, he triumphantly gave the world his third law, that the cubes of the planetary distances from the sun are as the squares of their periods of revolution around it. In transports of delight he wrote *De Harmonice Mundi* in which he published his third law. In a fever of imagi-

11

nation he speculated on the way the sun, the centre of the cosmos and therefore *nous* or Reason itself, apprehends the celestial music performed by the planets. Thus: 'Lulled by the changing harmony of the band of planets, there dwells in the sun an intellect simple, intellectual fire or mind, whatever it may be, the fountain of all harmony.' He even wrote down in musical notation the tune he ascribed to each planet.

His appreciation of the heavenly harmonies was to him a matter of ecstasy. His discoveries gave him passionate delight, a passion which blazes forth in a famous passage, where (having announced his third law, completing the trio describing exactly all planetary motion) he says:

What I prophesied two and twenty years ago, as soon as I discovered the five solids among the heavenly orbits – what I firmly believed long before I had seen Ptolemy's *Harmonics* – what I had promised my friends in the title of this book which I named before I was sure of my discovery, what sixteen years ago I urged to be sought – that for which I have devoted the best part of my life to astronomical contemplations, for which I joined Tycho Brahe, at last I have brought it to light and realized its truth beyond all my hopes. So now, since eighteen months ago the dawn, three months ago the proper light of day, and indeed a very few days ago the pure Sun itself, of the most marvellous contemplation, has shone forth – nothing holds me. I will indulge my sacred fury, I will taunt mankind with the confession that I have stolen the golden vases of the Egyptians to build of them a tabernacle to my God. If you forgive me I shall rejoice; if you are angry I shall bear it; the die is cast, the book is written, whether to be read now or by Posterity I care not. It may have to wait a hundred years for its reader, as God himself has waited six thousand years for a man to contemplate his work.*

Not for Kepler the cool detachment of the scientist of the popular image! Nor indeed for any scientist in the transports of

* Quoted in Polanyi, M., *Personal Knowledge*, University of Chicago Press, 1958, p. 7, from Proemium to Book V of *De Harmonice Mundi*.

discovery. It is strange that some scientists today seem ashamed of being human, so sedulously have they put it about that objectivity is their ideal, that they are passionless observers swayed not by emotion. Their protestations ring false in comparison with the ecstasy of Kepler.

The line of succession is from Copernicus, through Kepler and Galileo, to Newton. But before pursuing this, it is worth pausing to note the radical change in thinking that distinguished Newton's conception of natural motion from that of his predecessors. Aristotle had definite ideas on the interdependence between the distance moved by a body and the force exerted by the mover. To him it was a matter of common observation that the stronger the cause of the motion the farther the object was moved in a given time. Two men could move a stone twice as far in a given time as one man could. One man working alone could not move a heavy stone as far in a given time as a lighter stone. He took twice as long to move a certain stone a given distance as he took to move another only half its weight. These observations did not require any further explanation, for resistance to motion was also a self-evident fact of observation. Double the resistance, and the force required to sustain the motion was obviously twice as great. Rest was natural, motion was unnatural, in the sense that a cause of motion had to be sought. It was sustained motion that required scientific explanation. Rest needed none.

This was so obvious that it seemed eminently reasonable to suppose that the stars and planets were carried round on their daily paths by the agency of the heavenly spheres to which they were presumed to be attached. The celestial spheres themselves were moved by the Prime Cause of the universe. If this were not so they would inevitably come to rest, because rest was the natural order of things, and motion required sustaining. All common experience seemed to demonstrate the truth of this elementary principle.

To Galileo (1564–1642), on the contrary, it was not true. He believed that if resistance to motion could be progressively diminished, then ideally a body would continue longer and longer in its state of motion before coming to rest. To this extent Galileo could be said to have set the stage for Newton. But Galileo was still obsessed by the ideas of geometry. In particular he held it self-evident that natural motion, as such, must be circular. Only circular motion yields eternal order, endless repetition of a cycle of events. Motion in a straight line must be alien, since it involves change of place, unique and irrevocable; it must thus be symptomatic of disorder, and thus unnatural. To Galileo it seemed evident that nature was ordered, that order was cyclic, that all natural motion was eternal and therefore circular. If, he said, a ship could move on a windless ocean with no resistance to its passage through the water, it would keep on for ever. So far, so good. But naturally, thought Galileo, it would move in a circular path, a path which navigators call a Great Circle, i.e. a path which is a circle with its centre at the centre of the earth. This to Galileo was a truism, and required *no* demonstration. What, to him, would require explanation would be a failure of the ship to move for ever in this natural circular path. It was clear that the resistance to motion provided by the winds and the waves, and the viscous nature of the fluid in which it moved, was the cause of its defection from ideal behaviour; with this conclusion we should agree, but it is with the *form* of the ideal motion in a circle that we disagree, and in this we follow Newton.

All this was Galileo's inheritance from the Pythagorean tradition. At the same time he accepted the view, derived from Democritus, that the mechanical properties of things were primary, their other properties derivative or secondary. This view was to lead to Newtonian physics, and thence through Laplace to the dominance of the mechanistic picture of the universe.

To Newton (1642–1727), as to Galileo, the conception of ideal motion was equally necessary, and it was but the departures of bodies from the ideal that required explanation. But whereas Galileo thought it self-evident that the natural state of steady motion was circular, to Newton it was rectilinear. And in his first law of motion he stated this unambiguously. This idea was an abstract conception, for it means that all motion, as ordinarily observed, requires explanation. This is true not only of terrestrial motion which decays into stagnation and rest, under the influence of manifold resistances to movement; but also of the motions of the heavenly bodies, the planets perpetually circling about the sun, or the moon for ever wheeling captive to the earth.

Isaac Newton lived in rural isolation at his birthplace, Woolsthorpe Manor, Lincolnshire, from 1665 to 1667, while the University of Cambridge, from which he had just graduated, was closed because of the Great Plague. There he contemplated the problems of the universe, its construction and its action. According to his niece who recounted the story to Voltaire, the famous episode of the falling apple took place there. Newton, continually exercised in his mind concerning the causes of planetary motion, motion so exactly described by Kepler's three laws, was suddenly struck by the possibility that the moon and the apple, alike, were subject to the same force of gravity. That the apple fell towards the earth was an obvious fact of observation. That the moon was perpetually circling the earth was another. Was the moon in fact falling, just as the apple fell, but never getting any nearer because its fall was only just sufficient to keep it circling the earth? Newton had already calculated that the laws of Kepler required a central attracting force that decreased as the square of the distance of the satellite from the central body increased. Having had the flash of insight, he required only to calculate the ratio of the necessary forces on the apple and on the moon. This he did; and finding that, so far as he could tell, the ratio was just about right, he continued his speculations in private.

Seventeen years later, however, Edmund Halley (1656–1742), who afterwards became the second Astronomer Royal, formed the opinion while arguing with Christopher Wren and Robert Hooke that Kepler's third law of planetary motion required an attractive force between the sun and a planet varying as the

15

inverse square of the planetary distance. But though his guess was correct he could not prove it. When Hooke said that he himself could do so, Wren offered a prize of a forty-shilling book to whichever of the two brought him a proof within two months. At this Hooke said he would not disclose *his* solution so that others could attempt the problem – a transparent excuse that deceived no one! Halley, unable to solve the problem and doubting whether Hooke could do so either, journeyed to Cambridge to consult Newton. Bluntly coming to the point, he was astonished to find that Newton had already considered the problem and knew the answer. When Halley wished to know how he could be so certain, Newton told him that he had demonstrated by mathematical arguments that if gravity diminished as the square of the distance increased, the path of a planet must be an ellipse as Kepler had discovered it to be, and that the rate of description of the path satisfied Kepler's second and third laws also. Halley was enthralled, but Newton was unable to find his calculations, and to Halley's delight set about deriving the results afresh. Surprisingly enough, Newton's improvisation was a rigorous proof by an entirely new method. Halley was immensely impressed not only by Newton's genius and skill, but also by his indifference to publication of his discoveries. He begged Newton to give them to the world, and as a result Newton collected his works on gravity, spread over the past seventeen years, and drew up a course of lectures on the motion of bodies. This course Newton gave in 1684. By 1685 Halley had prevailed on Newton to write the first book of his great work. By the next summer the second book, and in 1687, the whole, of the *Principia* was published. Somewhat unfortunately the subject was treated geometrically, a method quite unsuited to dynamics. Newton's own invention, the differential calculus, or as he called it 'the method of fluxions', is far more suitable. For nearly two centuries many mathematicians laboured to reveal Newtonian mechanics in its full perfection of simplicity and power, but they added little to Newton's original discoveries.

The Marquis Pierre Simon de Laplace (1749–1827) published his *Mécanique Céleste* between 1799 and 1825. This great work, based on Newton's, presents the solar system as a stable mechanical system, in which all motions follow from the law of gravitational attraction between masses. Mathematical manipulation alone is sufficient to predict from simple premisses – that is, the masses and positions of the heavenly bodies at any instant – the ordered course of their motion, apparently for all time and with great success. Applied to the solar system, the method predicted the motions of the planets with astonishing precision; but as observational accuracy increased it became clear that there were slight discrepancies greater than could be accounted for merely as a consequence of inevitable experimental errors. This was chiefly noticeable in the motions of the outermost known planet, Uranus, which had been discovered by Herschel in 1781. The astronomer Arago (1786–1853) suggested that the matter was worth investigation; and Leverrier (1811–77), who in 1837 had become Professor of Astronomy in Paris, attacked the problem by postulating the existence of a still more distant but unknown planet whose gravitational action was perturbing the steady motion of Uranus. Independently John Couch Adams (1819–92), a young man later to become in 1858 Professor of Mathematics at St Andrews, made the same supposition; and, after making the necessary calculations, reported his belief to the Astronomer Royal. He stated that if search were made in the heavens in such and such a place at such and such a time, a hitherto unknown planet would be seen. He failed to obtain the assistance of any observer, and the frustration he experienced might well have soured his attitude to his fellow scientists; that it did not, is a tribute to his magnanimity. It was not until 1846, when Leverrier had announced his calculations (which were at once seen to agree with those of Adams), that serious search was made by Cambridge and European astronomers.

Challis at Cambridge actually observed the planet on four separate occasions during that summer, and once even recorded that the object seen seemed to have a sensible disc; but because he had no faith in the subject of his search he dismissed these observations as insignificant. Had he had the vision, enthusiasm, or imagination to believe his search worth while, he could have announced the discovery to the world before the astronomer Galle, who from the Berlin observatory on 23 September 1846 saw and recognized the planet for what it was. The success of the calculations was truly something to make the scientists and astronomers gasp with admiration. That from observations of minute irregularities of the motion of Uranus, a mathematician could infer the presence of an unobserved planet, and could moreover predict its exact position in the heavens at any given instant of time, was a surprising tribute to the accuracy of the original observations of Uranus, and also remarkable evidence of the truth of Newtonian mechanics and the exactness of operation of Newton's laws.

Of these brief glimpses of the development of mechanics from Aristotle to Copernicus, Kepler and Galileo, to Newton and Laplace, Leverrier and Adams, each has exemplified the utter commitment of the author to passionate belief in his ideas. Imagination has played round the problem until, in a flash of inspiration, a hypothesis has been formulated. Often, as with Kepler, the labour of deduction has been immense; with Leverrier, long drawn out; with Adams, lengthy, and the response frustrating and disheartening. Newton, singular in his hypersensitive fear of opposition and, worse, of criticism, was equally singular in his indifference to acclamation of success. He worked for weeks oblivious of his surroundings. It is recorded that in such moods he often sat on his bed ignorant of the passage of time, not knowing whether he had eaten or not, wrapt in contemplation of the problem in hand, indifferent to heat or cold, darkness or light, silence or noise, intent only on attaining a coherent pattern of truth. Few scientific discoverers are so vocal as Kepler, few so indrawn as Newton.

Chapter 2

FIELDS AND JOURNEYS

Max Born (1882–), one of the great mathematical physicists of this century, wrote: 'Faith, imagination and intuition are decisive factors in the progress of science as in any other human activity.'* Léon Brillouin, a distinguished mathematician, physicist and optician, Professor at Columbia University, New York, has recently written a book† which he dedicated in these words: 'An artist's inspiration or a scientist's theory, reveal the unpredictable power of human imagination.'

In the body of the book moreover,‡ in discussing the opinions of Max Planck, the inventor of the quantum theory, he says: 'Experiments are the only means of knowledge at our disposal. The rest is poetry, imagination.' Seeking to illustrate their theme, I have put forward the threefold thesis that the power of science derives from the qualities of a dedicated enthusiasm, an inspired imagination and a courageous perseverance in the teeth of apparent contradiction. Above all it was the inventive genius of great discoverers that enabled them to see, by the light of their inner vision, the form of things concealed from the eyes of men of less imagination. The originality that distinguishes a great scientist from his more pedestrian fellows, that lends potency to his dreams, vesting them with a substance and a reality denied to the shapeless phantoms of more sluggish minds, is to be ascribed to a ceaseless activity of his imagination, continually examining a problem from every angle. Isaac Newton said of himself that he differed nothing from

* Born, Max, *Natural Philosophy of Cause and Chance*. O.U.P., 1948, p. 209.
 † Brillouin, Léon, *Scientific Uncertainty and Information*. New York, Academic Press, 1964.
 ‡ ibid. p. 50

other men, but that he kept the subject of his inquiry constantly before him, and waited till the first dawning opened gradually, by little and little, into a full and clear light.

Newton was a physicist and mathematician of unique stature. The mathematics he invented, which he called the method of fluxions, which we know as the differential calculus, has been the most powerful weapon ever forged for the attack on the treasury of nature's secrets. Not only did he give us new mathematical tools, but he altered our conception of natural order, and stated the laws of motion governing the universe, from the solar system, the moon and the tides of the sea, to the apple orchard, the cricket field and the rifle range. More than any man he transformed our mode of thought.

Another man, of a different cast of mind, transformed our material civilization. But like Newton he owed his scientific eminence to the power of his imagination. This man was Michael Faraday (1791–1867). To his discoveries in electromagnetism we owe the means of production of electric power on an industrial scale, without which twentieth-century standards of living would differ little from those of the nineteenth century. But Faraday, like other men, built on other men's work. Newton said of his own labours that if he had seen further it was because he had stood on the shoulders of giants. Faraday, too, readily admitted his debt to his predecessors. His own discoveries have had vast consequences; but he owed the foundations of electrical knowledge to Oersted (1777–1851), Volta (1745–1827) and Galvani (1737–98), and, still earlier, to Benjamin Franklin, whose ideas deserve scrutiny.

Benjamin Franklin (1706–90) was a man of a very different character and temperament from those we have so far considered. His lower middle class origin in Boston, Mass., gave him a better worldly start than Michael Faraday, the blacksmith's son; and early in his life as a printer his liking for travel took him to London. Meeting there men of varied interests, some of a philosophic bent, he began to speculate widely, and often to commit his speculations to print. He returned to

America, became a publisher, a natural philosopher of no little insight, and the correspondent and personal friend of James Bowdoin (1727–90), at that time the first president of the newly formed American Academy of Arts and Sciences. He also became a statesman of repute, Envoy to England and Ambassador to France. It was Benjamin Franklin who corrected Thomas Jefferson's first draft of the Declaration of Independence. But more than for these lofty achievements he is remembered for the heating stove, bearing his name and still widely used; and he has the daily gratitude of those of us over middle age who use the bifocal eye-glasses he devised. Perhaps most of all are the farmers and the city burgesses indebted to him, for the lightning conductor he invented has so often preserved from destruction their barns, their town halls and churches.

It was Newton who first noted the similarity between the vivid lightning stroke in the vault of heaven, and the electric spark from resin rubbed with the fur of a cat – but, he added, 'on oh! how small a scale!' By 1750 others too had remarked the resemblance. But it was Franklin's inventive mind that seized on the implications of this likeness, perceiving that if the imagined similarity were indeed true, then existing knowledge of electrical phenomena, even that gained from petty experiments in the study or the parlour, was applicable to the immense meteorological displays in the skies. Franklin had discovered the action of metallic points in dissipating electric charges, and he set about obtaining such action on a large scale. He had hoped to conduct experiments at the top of a tall church tower which was at that time under construction in Philadelphia. Then, as now, there were building delays, and he was forced to change his plans. Instead of the tower, he used a kite to carry a pointed metal rod high into the sky during a thunderstorm. As he had predicted, he drew electrical sparks from the kite-string. His action was as bold as his imagination was vivid, but he was fortunate in the outcome. He did not realize the danger of the experiment, which created intense interest and excitement, and which was repeated on the continent of Europe to the delight of the onlookers, until two experimenters were killed by lightning stroke. Franklin had successfully proved his point, and thenceforward the principle of the lightning-conductor was widely applied.*

Many of his experiments contributed significantly to our knowledge of electricity. He made an exhaustive study of electrostatic induction of charges, and of the action of the Leyden jar, or electric condenser. He discovered that the thinner the glass of the jar the larger its electrical capacity, and from his experiments he drew the correct conclusion that the charge resided, not in the metallic coatings, but in the glass. In every physics laboratory teaching fundamental physics today, his dissectible Leyden jar is still in use to demonstrate that the seat of the energy lies in the electrically polarized glass.

As the result of many careful experiments, Franklin came to have very clear ideas on the nature of electricity; his explanation of electrical phenomena is fundamentally identical with that given by modern theory. He imagined all matter as being of two kinds, one ponderable, the other imponderable; the one massy, the other too subtle to be detected by a balance. For its own kind each experienced repulsion, while at the same time attracting its opposite. Both kinds coexisted in all bodies; when electrically uncharged, a body possessed equal quantities of each. When two bodies were rubbed together, friction caused a transfer of the more subtle sort of matter from one to the other so that both exhibited electrification, though of opposite kinds. At that time the two states of electrification that can be produced were known respectively as vitreous and resinous electrification – names arising from the typical means of producing them, by rubbing either glass or amber. Franklin denoted as *positive* the state of electrification of a body having an

* He caused a copy of his account of his electrical experiments to be made and sent to his friend James Bowdoin, and this signed copy is in the archives of the American Academy of Arts and Sciences at Boston, Mass.

excess of the subtle, imponderable matter; the state of the other, having a deficiency, he denoted as *negative*. For us it is perhaps slightly unfortunate that he chose to designate vitreous electrification as positive, since we now know that the massive part of matter is associated with what Franklin called positive, and the subtler part of matter, today known as the electron, with what he chose to think of as negative. But this is a trivial detail of nomenclature.

In the language of the time, the subtle imponderable component of matter was termed a fluid, so Franklin's view became known as the one-fluid theory of electrification. In contrast to the more complicated two-fluid theory that had been propounded in Europe by du Fay (1698–1739), Franklin's had the advantage of simplicity; it also had the supreme merit of postulating the fundamental nature of electricity, and the intimate relationship between massive matter and subtle electricity. It emphasized Franklin's belief that the study of electricity would reveal the nature of matter itself – a faith that has illuminated science from that time on, and has guided physics to its present pinnacle of achievement.

Franklin wrote his own epitaph, as is well known, for it is inscribed on the stone near his grave in Philadelphia. To quote so flawless a gem needs no apology:

The Body of
B. Franklin Printer
Like the Cover of an old Book
Its Contents torn out
And stript of its Lettering and Gilding
Lies here, Food for Worms.
But the Work shall not be lost
For it will (as he believed) appear once more
In a new and more elegant Edition
Revised and corrected by the Author.

He has no need of other monument. His most lasting memorial is his one-fluid theory of electricity on which modern electrical science is based, of which a recent biographer, Bernard Cohen of Harvard, wrote that 'having served to advance physical science in the eighteenth century, it was not buried in old books lying on library shelves "food for worms", but one hundred and fifty years after its creation it appeared "again, in a new and more elegant edition".'*

To Franklin's insight we owe the foundations of our knowledge of static electricity; the later discoveries by Galvani and Volta provided the sources of current electricity required for nineteenth-century researches now to be considered. In 1813 Michael Faraday, the son of a blacksmith in Newington Butts, London, had become laboratory assistant to Sir Humphrey Davy at the Royal Institution; twenty years later he succeeded him as Fullerian Professor of Chemistry. In 1831 Faraday's experiments – brilliantly conceived and skilfully executed – together with his remarkable insight, laid bare the fundamentals of electromagnetism; and from then on, almost every year he brought to light some new phenomenon in this field. His astonishing fertility in experimental research may be ascribed to his vivid imagination, for he had a genius for formulating hypotheses by means of the most picturesque concepts. He was entirely without mathematical skill, but his power of explaining phenomena in visual terms was unique. The extraordinary facility he possessed of forming mental images with which to interpret his observations gave him food for contemplation from whence he drew inspiration for new experiments.

To a remarkable degree the growth of science has depended on the scientist's faculty of mental imagery, of making, as it were, models to simulate the behaviour of the observable world. Magnetism, for example, was known to the Chinese as early as the end of the eleventh century, and soon afterwards pieces of the mineral magnetite, a natural magnet, were in use as lodestones, a primitive form of navigational compass. But it was not until the time of the first Elizabethan age that a funda-

* Cohen, B. I., *Franklin and Newton*. American Philosophical Society Press, Philadelphia, 1956.

24

mental advance was made with the publication by William Gilbert of his treatise *De Magnete*. He imagined the earth to be a vast magnet, and to prove his point fashioned *terrellae*, little spheres of magnetite, which he used to simulate the effect of the earth upon a compass needle. A terrella was a model in a real mechanical sense, but it is only a short step from such inventions to the imagery of Franklin or of Faraday. Franklin described the process of giving an electric charge to an insulated body as the addition or subtraction of a quantity of a subtle fluid. No doubt this was more a matter of words than of images, whereas Faraday's concepts were, as we shall see, startlingly visual and appealed directly to the mind's eye.

The ability to construct mental pictures and to argue by analogy therefrom has been a conspicuous characteristic of physicists and chemists, and to a lesser extent biologists also. (The latter are perhaps less dependent on mental pictures because their microscopes daily fill their bodily eyes with visual images of such wonder and beauty.) We are tempted to think the more vivid the vision the more dramatic the ensuing scientific advance. It is often notable how close is the correspondence between the first crude and improbable guess and the later more refined versions of the model. Consider for example the benzene ring of organic chemistry, postulated by Friedrich August Kekulé (1829–96) in 1865. His original conception that molecules of aromatic substances are formed of chains of atoms coiled in a ring, like the snake eating its own tail, that he saw in a half-waking dream as he slumbered before the fire, is still unchanged today. Though Kekulé himself never doubted his vision, and its essential truth was soon accepted by most chemists, it had to wait until they could use the physicists' methods of wave-mechanical calculation before the theoretical stability of the ring structure could be established with certainty.

As an illustration from biology we may think of the genes which were proposed to account for the Mendelian laws of heredity. They were concepts of fundamental importance, but they had no clear visual counterpart until optical studies of

25

chromosomes suggested that they must be connected with some kind of dimly perceived helical structure. Modern X-ray diffraction, aided by electron microscopy, has now shown that the amino-acids responsible for transmission of genetic information from one generation of living cells to the next weave themselves into a fabric like a double helix, each turn of the helix being associated with a different genetic factor. The genes of the original hypothesis have become almost visible entities.

These examples serve to point the argument, but it is with Michael Faraday's contributions that we are here concerned, for much in modern physical thought derives directly from his vivid imagery; it was in his mind that the idea of fields of force was conceived, an idea which plays so large a part in physical theories of today.

Let us recall the history of mechanics and the development of the concept of force. Originally the phenomenon that all unsupported bodies fall downward was naïvely ascribed to an innate property they possessed, that of *gravitas* or heaviness, the natural consequence being downward motion. Newton meditating on the labours of Copernicus, Kepler and Galileo perceived that this same gravitas kept the moon circling in its course round the earth, and the planets in their orbits round the sun; he inferred from this that all bodies attracted each other with a force proportional to the product of their masses and to the inverse square of their distance apart. How this force was exerted was unknown, and to both Newton and his contemporaries was a great puzzle. To most minds, action between bodies in contact presents no problem, but action at a distance is incomprehensible. Dr Samuel Johnson controverted the idealistic philosophy of Bishop Berkeley by kicking a stone: the sensation that he had of the interaction between the toe of his boot and the stone was to him convincing evidence of the reality of the stone, so that it seemed unnecessary to question *how* these two, the stone and his boot, exerted force on one another. In point of fact, contiguous action is just as hard to explain as action at a distance, but psychologically it presents less of a problem. Although on several occasions Newton entertained speculations concerning the manner in which gravitational action at a distance comes about, he usually maintained an agnostic attitude. But Michael Faraday, studying the interaction of magnets or of electrical charges, was intolerant of such agnosticism. Benjamin Franklin had already elucidated the phenomenon of electrostatic induction of charge, and had shown the glass of an electrically charged Leyden jar to be the seat of the energy. Faraday repeated and extended his experiments. He observed the motions of electrically charged bodies, and of magnets, and he sought an explanation in terms of forces between them, just as the principles of Newtonian mechanics bade him. But Faraday could not rest content with the bare concept of forces – he had to form in his mind a picture of their origin. To him it appeared as if the magnets, or the charged bodies, were surrounded by a kind of aura, in which the mechanical motions followed just as if the magnets were connected by elastic strings. These invisible, insubstantial strings – Faraday called them lines of force – were the aura itself, and were indissolubly attached to the magnet. They were somewhat like the bright rays in an artist's drawing of a star; or, to use a less elegant but more vigorous simile, like the tentacles of an octopus capable of forcibly moving whatever they touched.

This was an hypothesis of great merit, but could it be substantiated? It occurred to Faraday that, if the space between two magnets or two electrical charges were in fact filled with such invisible elastic tentacles, then it would be under compression just as surely as a transparent jelly would be when squashed between two solid plates. Now at that time Sir David Brewster (1781–1868) of St Andrews, and later of Edinburgh, had recently shown that a transparent substance under stress of compression or extension, underwent an optical change so that it became doubly refracting like many natural crystals, and in polarized light could give rise to brilliant colours. Today, engineers wishing to discover and measure the stresses in their

27

structures, make of them transparent models, and use just this effect which Brewster discovered. A hundred and forty years ago Faraday tried by means of this same effect to demonstrate the existence of stress in the space between his magnets. He was bitterly disappointed, and temporarily puzzled, because he failed to find any such evidence. We know that this was not because his deductions were at fault, but because his methods of detection were not sufficiently sensitive and his electromagnets too weak. The results he sought were ultimately found in 1875 by Kerr, and in 1898 by Cotton and Mouton. Faraday abandoned his experiments, but returned to them fifteen years later, when – changing his manner of attack – he succedeed in discovering an allied phenomenon that he had not precisely foreseen. This was the magneto-optical effect, known now as the Faraday effect, which he immediately saw to be far-reaching in its consequences, for at one and the same time it showed both light and matter to be electrical and magnetic in character.

But to return to Faraday's concept of an aura or field of force surrounding a magnet or an electric charge. The idea was picturesque, and Faraday used it to the full; but as he lacked mathematical skill, the theory – in the absence of mathematical treatment – remained only qualitative. Twenty years later James Clerk Maxwell (1831–79) translated Faraday's pictorial concepts into mathematical terms. His imagination was of a different kind from Faraday's; whereas Faraday thought of his lines of force like elastic strings under tension, Maxwell sought to make them obey the same laws as the stream-lines in a flowing liquid. Streaming fluids must obey a rule known as the equation of continuity, which says, in effect, that what goes in must come out. But the equations Maxwell had derived contradicted it, and he saw that this would never do. So, to put matters right, he invented a new quantity, which he called a displacement current. The equation of continuity was satisfied, but now an astonishing result tumbled out of his modified equations. Waves are common in fluids; Faraday's fields had been made to obey the laws of fluids – so perhaps it was no wonder that

Maxwell's electro-magnetic equations showed that the fields must exhibit waves. It remained only to calculate, from the known constants of electric and magnetic phenomena, the velocity of travel of these waves. It was 186,000 miles a second! Maxwell, daring to build on Faraday's vision, had demonstrated that there must exist electromagnetic waves, and that they travelled with a velocity already well known, for it was exactly that at which light travelled. Imaginative thinking of a picturesque variety had stimulated the more abstract imagination of a skilled mathematician and led to an astonishing conclusion. It was tantalizing that no experimental test seemed feasible.

Maxwell was not good at explanation and some of his writings are remarkably obscure. Heinrich Hertz (1857–94) was one of many fascinated by Maxwell's ideas, but he often found them impossible to follow, and he is said to have once exclaimed in exasperation: 'Maxwell's theory is – Maxwell's equations.' However, the theory was well founded, for in 1886 Hertz discovered the waves now named after him, and known to everyone as radio waves. These are produced electromagnetically, and are obviously of the same nature as light, differing from light only in having wavelengths thousands of millions of times longer than light waves. To research workers in laboratories these electromagnetic waves opened new fields of study, and were quickly applied to provide new means of telegraphic communication, without the need for connecting wires between the sender and the receiver. The English still call such means of communication 'wireless', and the French 'télégraphie sans fil'. As these wireless waves were believed to travel in straight lines, they were thought to be useless except for short distances, because over long distances the curvature of the earth would hide the sending from the receiving station. Everyone knows how Marconi – with a perseverance worthy of a true scientist – disregarded all arguments, and persisted in trying to transmit the waves across the Atlantic, with dramatic success. The experiment, which the scientists were certain must fail, succeeded spectacularly. The waves were bounced round the earth by reflexion from electrically conducting layers in the upper atmosphere. Marconi not only showed long distance radio communication to be possible, but he revealed the hitherto unsuspected existence of ionization in the upper atmosphere, later found to be caused by radiation from the sun and from outer space. To pursue the ramifications of these subjects further would uncover numerous examples of ingenious applications of physics to daily life. These might well illustrate our basic theme, but we must keep to the main paths of discovery of fundamental principles.

The work of Maxwell was generalized by another mathematical physicist, H. A. Lorentz (1853–1928), who, during the last decade of the century, extended it to cover the consequences of motion of electric charges, or of magnets. But the mathematical equations of the motion of moving charges provided contradictions, the chief of which, in simple terms, was that the action of a moving magnet on a stationary electric charge appeared to be different from the action of a moving electric charge on a stationary magnet. This is in flat contradiction to Newton's third law: that action and reaction must always be equal and opposite. This law is the cornerstone of Newtonian mechanics, and we still firmly believe it to be universally applicable. It is unthinkable to reject it.

Closely related to this difficulty in formulating the laws of electrodynamics is another paradox which arose from consideration of the motion of an observer. Arago suggested in 1817 that careful measurement of the passage of light through any optical instrument should reveal differences depending on the direction of the path of the light relative to the motion of the instrument through space, as this is carried in the laboratory round the sun at the rate of some twenty miles a second. This may seem to be a great speed, but as light travels nearly 200,000 miles in the same time, the ratio of the two speeds is very small, and the effect is correspondingly minute. In America in 1887 Michelson (1852–1931) and Morley devised an instrument sufficiently sensitive to make the detection of this effect possible. But to everyone's surprise no effect was found – at least, measurements showed a variation far smaller than had been predicted. To account for this an Irish physicist Fitzgerald (1851–1901) suggested that, as a consequence of its motion, the apparatus might have contracted in the direction of motion by exactly the right amount to nullify the optical change. Lorentz also, from considering the movement of matter in electromagnetic fields, obtained transformation equations from which the Fitzgerald contraction followed. Such strange behaviour on the part of nature seemed a mean trick to obstruct the scientist in his attempt to discover her secrets! Everyone was perplexed and unhappy at this curious state of affairs.

Einstein, as a schoolboy of sixteen, was struck by the electrodynamic paradox, and for ten years he puzzled over it. He was profoundly influenced by Ernst Mach's contention that Newtonian mechanics was based on a special conception of space, and on the idea of absolute rest in space; and that because these concepts could not be tested by experiment they were meaningless. Mach had urged that Newtonian mechanics should be reformulated so as to avoid the idea of motion, except that of the relative motion of bodies with respect to each other. Lorentz and Henri Poincaré (1854–1912) both came to the conclusion that by no experiment could an observer discover his own absolute motion in space, but could only observe relative motion between himself and other objects. Einstein, pondering on electrodynamics, also came to the same conclusion. In his great paper on the electrodynamics of moving bodies he stated the postulates of the theory of Relativity. The first was that 'the phenomena of electromagnetism, as well as those of mechanics, possess no properties corresponding to the idea of absolute rest'; from which it followed that the action of a moving magnet on a stationary electric charge is equal and opposite to the action of a moving electric charge on a stationary magnet. There is in fact no meaning in the words stationary and moving; one ought to say rather that the

31

action between a magnet and an electric charge depends only on their relative motion. Einstein's second postulate was that 'light is always propagated in empty space with a velocity independent of the state of motion of the source'. From these two postulates, and from precise consideration of the methods available for measuring space and time, Einstein derived the Lorentz transformation equations. This was remarkable. To have started from considerations of electrodynamics, and to have obtained equations predicting the result of an optical experiment was astonishing enough, but it further transpired that Einstein's theory contained within itself the explanation of many other physical observations. To crown all, Maxwell's equations, which had proved so satisfactory in describing electromagnetic and optical phenomena, remained unaltered.

The success of Einstein's theory was not unchallenged, for there were difficulties of interpretation, and the conclusions were not acceptable to everyone. Indeed, physicists were sharply divided into two camps, one enthusiastically supporting the theory, the other bitterly critical. The hostility of the opposition had the curious effect of suppressing the scepticism that one might have expected even from adherents. Dayton C. Miller, of the Case Institute in Cleveland, Ohio, repeated the Michelson-Morley experiment over a period of years; at a meeting of the American Physical Society in 1925 he reported that the result was by no means the null that had been claimed. The result was small, but it was not zero. Yet the response was not what might have been expected, for the audience in no way abandoned its acceptance of the theory of relativity. No one doubted the sincerity of the experimenters, nor the meticulous care taken to ensure the highest accuracy attainable; it was simply taken for granted that later experiments, or a new analysis of the results, would reveal some unperceived source of error and that in the end the theory would be vindicated. Time has justified this attitude, even though sporadic controversy still arises.

A gument flared up some years ago over a difficulty which came into prominence in consequence of the technical successes of rocket propulsion, which, fantastic as it now seems, might one day make it possible to travel at high speeds through vast distances of space for long periods of time. A brief discussion of the problem may be of interest.

Consider two observers, one on earth, the other travelling in a space-ship. Einstein's theory of relativity, applicable to uniform motion, destroys the distinction between two such observers, so that it becomes meaningless to say of either that one is moving and the other not. All that we are entitled to say is that there is relative motion between them. Neither is in a privileged position, neither can tell whether the other be at rest, for a state of rest is but a meaningless phrase. To describe the happenings in the environment of either as seen by the other, we have to apply the Lorentz transformations, which tell us that, as seen by either observer, the dimensions of the other appear to shrink in the direction of their common line of sight. Moreover, as seen by either, clocks carried by the other appear to run slow, and this slowing down is independent of the direction of motion, i.e. it is the same whether they are approaching or receding from each other.

Now suppose that the two observers are originally close together, but that one sets off on a journey into space, ultimately returning to a rendezvous with the other. Will the time taken for the journey appear to be the same to both of them? Let each carry with him an accurate clock by which he may measure the lapse of time. If each compares the time measured on his own clock with that he sees recorded on the other's, the Lorentz transformations tell us that the time either observer will think has elapsed is longer than that indicated by the clock carried by the other. They cannot *both* be right! Does this mean that the theory is wrong? Is the theory self-contradictory, as some critics have maintained? The error lies in the premiss. The special theory of relativity applies only to systems in *uniform* motion, and one at least of the observers must suffer acceleration if he is first to remove from the proximity of his fellow, and then to return to a mutual rendezvous with him. If he is a space-traveller and his fellow an earth-bound stay-at-home, the symmetry of the problem has vanished. The states of motion of the two observers are not now indistinguishable, for one of them is subject to acceleration, while the other is not. Analysis of *this* situation shows that the clocks of the stay-at-home will register a greater lapse of time than will the clocks carried by the traveller. This has been interpreted as indicating that the traveller ages more slowly than his brother on earth. Curiously enough, a naïve application of the Lorentz transformations, assuming the stay-at-home to be in the privileged position, gives exactly the same result as the general theory proper to the problem; what is lost by neglecting the acceleration is made up by assuming the velocity to be constant over the whole period of the journey. Because various points in the argument have not always been appreciated, heated controversy has raged over the problem, which has come to be known as the 'twin paradox'. When it becomes possible to make a voyage of sufficient duration in a space-ship this should settle the matter. But it will have to be a very fast space-ship, and it will have to make the full return journey (which no doubt the travellers will hope for!) if the experiment is to be convincing. In theory, it is not necessary for human beings to make the journey, for we could test the question by sending an atomic clock on an excursion into space; but it must make a full return journey, and there must be no interruption of the clock *en route*. It seems unlikely that proof will come just yet.

For one-way travellers the relativistic dilation of time has been confirmed by observations of cosmic rays. When they enter the atmosphere of our earth these rays from outer space may, on colliding with molecules of air, produce short-lived particles called mesons.* These travel towards the surface of the earth with a speed nearly that of light. However, they decay rapidly and the duration of their brief existence is accurately

* See p. 70.

34

known. Because we know where they are formed, and because we know their speed, the time required for their journey from their place of origin to our recording instruments on the surface of the earth can be calculated. This turns out to be about fifteen times longer than their life! Yet they most certainly live long enough to reach the earth and there operate the recorders. The paradox is solved if the Lorentz transformations be applied to the problem. The mesons are travelling fast, and the consequent dilation of their time-scale is great enough to expand their life sufficiently for them to survive the journey. To put it another way, if an observer travelling with the meson were to measure the depth of the atmosphere below him, he would find that it would appear to have contracted, and to be so shallow, that, at his speed of travel, he would have ample time to reach the earth within the short time the meson lasts. This is indeed an Alice-in-Wonderland state of affairs and you may think that scientific imagination has got the better of sanity. Maybe! It is just one example out of many others that the behaviour of small high-speed particles must not be judged by the rules of everyday human life.

The most convincing of all experimental support for the special theory of relativity are the facts of nuclear fission and fusion. From the theory it follows that the energy E associated with any mass m is mc^2, and as c (the velocity of light) is very large, i.e. 300,000 kilometers a second, the energy released when mass, even a very small mass, is annihilated is very great. When in Germany in 1939 a group of scientists, Otto Hahn (1879–), Lise Meitner (1878–) and her nephew Frisch (1904–), researching on the phenomena of induced radioactivity, discovered the fission of uranium, it was clear that they had revealed vast potentialities for good, and for evil. Einstein, a life-long pacifist, who thirty-five years before had deduced the equation $E = mc^2$, felt it his duty to warn Roosevelt, then President of the United States, that an atomic bomb was a possibility. The results – Hiroshima and Nagasaki, atomic fission bombs, and now hydrogen fusion bombs – are only too well known. Man's knowledge is better than his judgement. His scientific imagination is strong, but his political control is weak.

All the predictions of the special theory of relativity have been the subject of experimental tests; usually, the better the precision of the experiment, the better the verification, though there has often been room for much detailed argument. For instance, the mass of swiftly moving particles is greater than the mass of the same particles moving slowly, and the daily operation of the numerous particle-accelerators in nuclear laboratories the world over is a witness to this fact. Even so, the exactness with which the relativistic formula holds good is less than is generally supposed, according to a recent review of the evidence.*

Verification of the predictions of the general theory of relativity has been difficult, for the only three there are have been hard to test. Deflexion of light in a gravitational field has been measured by astronomers by photographing the stars at the edge of the disc of the sun during a total eclipse. The experimental difficulties are numerous, and it is not surprising that the results are sometimes found to fit and sometimes not. The running-slow of clocks in a gravitational field has been tested by making spectroscopic observations of the light emitted from super-dense stars. An atom is a kind of natural clock, and if such a clock runs slow the light it emits is lowered in frequency. This is the cause of the so-called red-shift (or reddening of the light emitted) in a gravitational field, but there are so many unknown factors that the results, although qualitatively correct, do not give sufficiently exact quantitative agreement to provide convincing corroboration of the theory.

Radioactive atomic nuclei may also serve as natural clocks since they emit γ-rays of definite frequency. Resonance occurs between two nuclei, the one emitting and the other absorbing a γ-ray. This provides means by which the most minute change in nuclear frequency may be detected, as a young research worker in Germany discovered. The Mossbäuer effect, called after its

* Farago and Janossy, Nuovo Cimento (1957) 5, p. 1411.

discoverer, has been used to measure the extremely minute change in nuclear frequency resulting from the slight variation in the gravitational field at different heights above sea-level. Observations recently made at Princeton, New Jersey, have given results in very precise agreement with predictions from relativity theory. The accuracy is so good that the measurements are considered to provide one of the most stringent tests of the theory.

The third test of the general theory of relativity is in fact the earliest one and was available to Einstein himself. Relativistic equations for the motion of a planet in its orbit, as it speeds up and slows down again in its elliptic path, yield a small correction to predictions from the Newtonian theory of gravitation. The result is a very slow precession of the perihelion of the orbit. The rate of precession is unnoticeable for the more distant planets, but for the innermost, fastest moving and most accelerated planet, Mercury, the precession has been detected and amounts to a rotation of forty-three seconds of angle per century. This is of the order of magnitude of the theoretical prediction, and though the agreement leaves something to be desired, for some years it provided the sole experimental support for the general theory. On the atomic scale a similar precession is to be expected in the motion of an electron round the nucleus, and this gives rise to a fine structure of the spectral lines. This fine structure has been observed in the spectra of light emitted from hydrogen and hydrogen-like atoms. In this case agreement between theory and experiment is exact.

The fact that experimental results have not invariably accorded with theoretical predictions is perhaps responsible for the acrimony of the controversies. Protagonists hold their views with almost religious fervour. If scientists were consistently the logical positivists they sometimes believe themselves to be, contradictions between theory and the early experiments might long ago have forced a renunciation of the theory. Fortunately they are too convinced of the inherent rationality of the theory of Relativity to abandon it. Always the theory has been adhered to in the hope that newer measurements would give better agreement; in the meantime the elegant beauty of the theoretical edifice is thought sufficient reason for believing it to be true. Dirac has said: 'It is more important to have beauty in one's equations than to have them fit the experiment. . . . One should not be discouraged if there is not complete agreement between the results of one's work and experiment, because the discrepancy may well be due to minor features that are not properly taken into account.'* Ernst Mach would have found this statement shocking, but I suggest that we may think it shows a proper belief in the rationality of the universe and a faith in the humanity of science.

* Dirac, P.A.M., 'The Physicist's Picture of Nature' in *Scientific American*, 208 (May 1960), p. 45.

Chapter 3

WAVES AND PARTICLES

Max Planck, whose invention of quantum theory has, in this twentieth century, revolutionized scientific thought, said: 'The pioneer scientist must have a vivid intuitive imagination for new ideas, ideas not generated by deduction, but by *artistically* creative imagination.'* In this book my thesis has been that discoveries in science have been the fruits of an active and vigorous imagination, that discoverers are men whose creative intellect, restlessly seeking understanding of the universe, owes achievement to inspiration and vaulting foresight. Furthermore, it is their enthusiastic commitment to the pursuit of truth that enables them to keep their vision undimmed even though for a space failure should seem inevitable. But not all scientists are great discoverers. Even eminent men may be sometimes blind. Practical men have been known to be more concerned with past achievements and present applications of knowledge, than with future developments. Such a tendency seemed especially evident at the end of the nineteenth century. The growth of scientific knowledge had been so stupendous, technical achievement had already been so great, and so much more was promised, that it is perhaps not surprising that a certain smug satisfaction clouded the vision of some of those who were ageing with the century.

One of the great physicists of the nineteenth century was William Thomson (1824–1907), famous for work in the fields of electricity and thermodynamics. He was knighted and later ennobled by Queen Victoria for the eminence and importance of his contributions to science, particularly to applied science.

* Planck, Max, *Autobiography*. Translation by Frank Gaynor. American Philosophical Library, New York, 1949, p. 109.

But Sir William Thomson, later Lord Kelvin, so able a physicist, so active in the application of scientific discoveries to practical matters (from the methods of measurement of electrical quantities to the manufacture and laying of transatlantic telegraph cables), whose memory is perpetuated in the names not only of phenomena he discovered, and of apparatus he invented, but of scientific manufacturing firms that he founded or directed, was curiously unable to see the endless vistas that science offered to the imagination. The thoroughness of his mathematical grasp left him little inkling of the limitations science must suffer unless it comes under the liberating influence of the creative imagination of men more visionary than he. For example, on the assumption that the sun was in a state of thermal equilibrium in which the outward pressure, resulting from the high temperature of the gases in the interior, was balanced by the inward force of its own gravity, he calculated that the maximum age of the sun as a useful source of warmth for the maintenance of life on this earth was but twenty-four million years. In support of this estimate, he considered the rate of cooling of the earth. From laboratory measurements of the thermal conductivity of various rocks, he drew the conclusion that the earth must have been a ball of molten lava no more than forty, and probably no more than twenty, million years ago. The approximate agreement between the two estimates arrived at by two quite different arguments seemed to him entirely convincing, and in consequence he was dogmatic in his opposition to the geologists, who were equally certain from their observations of the present rate of erosion of the earth's surface that the age of the earth was many hundreds of times greater.

To Kelvin this indicated that the geologists were wrong, not that his mathematical physics, which was correct enough, had started from false premises. He made his views the subject of his presidential address to the British Association for the Advancement of Science in 1897. By an irony of fate only the previous year Henri Becquerel (1852–1908) had discovered the phenomenon of radioactivity that was to lead the Curies to isolate radium two years later. The presence of an unknown quantity of radioactive material in the core of the earth, continuously engendering heat, rendered any estimate of age made from thermal considerations completely untrustworthy. Rutherford's researches in radioactivity, of which I shall write later, led to the discovery of the fission and fusion of the nuclei of atoms, and to the knowledge that there existed almost limitless sources of energy in the sun and in all the stars. The life of the sun was no longer determined by the rate of gravitational collapse as Kelvin had thought, but was based on what has come to be known as the carbon cycle of nuclear interactions, whereby hydrogen nuclei condense to form helium, and liberate vast quantities of heat in the depths of the sun's interior. With these discoveries, Kelvin's accurately made calculations (false because the assumptions were false, having been made from incomplete knowledge) passed into the waste-heap of scientific mistakes.

This is but one instance. Another was Kelvin's prophecy that the physicist of the twentieth century would be concerned only with measurements of ever-increasing accuracy; with the more minute study of existing phenomena; and with the addition of yet one more decimal place to the precision with which their forerunners had made their preliminary determinations of constants. The laws of physics having been discovered, it remained only to make the quantitative knowledge more and more exact. Now, no scientist can deny the value of accurate measurement; we have seen instances where the most minute discrepancy between prediction and observation has led to new discoveries. But necessary as it is to push exactness of measurement to the limit, how little can this precision achieve unless illuminated by the genius of imagination. Before we go on to substantiate this, it is worth remarking that Max Planck, who died in 1947 after a long life of inspired activity in physics, sought guidance from his seniors at the opening of his own career. He was advised to avoid physics, which was then thought

41

to be played out, in which everything interesting had already been discovered, and which held no future for a man of ambition; rather should he turn his attention elsewhere, to physiology or medicine. Fortunately, he rejected the advice.

The guess that biology was to be a field of remarkable advances, was to prove accurate enough, even though delayed by nearly half a century; that, at the end of the nineteenth century, the prophetic insight was clouded where physics was concerned, is now common knowledge. The turn of the century brought three major developments, one of which, Relativity, was one of the topics of Chapter 2. The other two are the Quantum Theory and Nuclear Physics. It is with the conception and birth of the former that I now wish to concern myself.

It is necessary to remark that the understanding of optics had progressed rapidly after Thomas Young (1773–1829), in 1800, had devised convincing experiments clearly demonstrating that light was a wave-motion of some kind. The next forty-five years witnessed the detailed development of the wave theory of light; but it was not until after 1845, when Michael Faraday discovered the magneto-optical effect, that any reasonable guess could be made as to what in fact was waving. When Maxwell put forward his electro-magnetic theory, and when subsequently Hertz produced electromagnetic waves in the laboratory, it became clear that the picture was coherent, and that all radiation, whether of light, heat, or Hertzian waves, was of waves of the electromagnetic field in space. Waves are characterized by two quantities, velocity and frequency. In free space the velocity of all electromagnetic waves is the same, but the spectrum of frequency ranges from the lowest values, reckoned in thousands per second, to as much as a hundred million million million per second for X-rays and γ-rays. The spectral distribution of energy throughout this vast range of possible frequencies is a matter of great interest, both experimental and theoretical.

The development of thermodynamics, which concerns the mathematical treatment of fundamental processes of heat transfer and of the transformation of energy between its various

42

forms, owes much to Lord Kelvin. Application of the principles, which were seen to be of universal importance, had been made by many thinkers to the general problem of radiation of heat and light. The successes of the method were many. Boltzmann (1844–1906), in particular, had developed ideas of statistics which, when combined with thermodynamical principles, led to the explanation and to the quantitative description of some of the laws of radiation. The Stefan-Boltzmann law relating the total energy radiated by any body to its absolute temperature was one such success. The heat and light radiated by the walls of a hollow body maintained at a definite temperature, are characteristic only of this temperature. Define the temperature, and the radiation is completely defined, both as regards its intensity and the distribution of energy amongst the whole range of possible frequencies. This distribution of energy against frequency may be thought of as the spectral colour of the radiation. Just as a hot iron may be only at a black heat, or at a dull red one; as a still hotter furnace may be at a bright red heat, or one still hotter at a white heat; as an electric spark may be blue in colour, or the flash from a nuclear bomb most intense in the ultra-violet or X-ray region of the spectrum; so in precise terms it is found that the spectral colour is exactly defined by the temperature. But the most surprising result of applying the principles of thermodynamics to the problem of radiation was its failure – the utter contradiction between theory and experiment; or to be specific, exact agreement for low-frequency radiation, total disagreement for high frequencies. Lord Rayleigh (1842–1919) and Sir James Jeans (1877–1946), both physicists and mathematicians of great ability, agreed in finding this total disagreement between theory and observation. Very careful experiments had been made in 1899 by Lummer and Pringsheim to establish with the highest accuracy the distribution of energy throughout the spectrum. Their results, which are indisputable today, were obstinately in flat contradiction to theory.

An attempt had been made by Wien to modify the result of

43

thermodynamical reasoning by making certain rather doubtful assumptions concerning the manner of emission of radiation. This had yielded a theoretical formula which was more acceptable, in that it was not in such obvious and violent contradiction with observations; but when compared with the careful measurements of Lummer and Pringsheim, it was found to be still wide of the truth. Curiously enough, although it was near the mark for high frequencies, where the Rayleigh-Jeans formula was wildly wrong, it was demonstrably wrong at low frequencies where the Rayleigh-Jeans formula was right.

Although the dilemma lasted but a few months, until 1900, it is necessary to pause here to explain what a complete change in thought had to come before the hypothesis which was to yield the correct description could be formulated, let alone receive a sympathetic hearing. Newtonian mathematics, the method of fluxions, owed its power to the basic concept of infinitesimal increments. To put this another way, it was of universal application because it dealt with quantities which by their nature could be considered to vary in continuous fashion; hence mathematical arguments could be applied by considering ever smaller and smaller increments, or decrements, without limit to their minuteness. A familiar example of this is the solution of the age-old problem, sometimes called 'squaring the circle'; which involves finding the ratio between the lengths of the circumference and the diameter. We can very easily find the ratio between the perimeter of any regular figure and its diagonal. For a square, it is nearly three to one; for a hexagon, exactly three to one; for a dodecagon a little more than three to one, and so on. We can continue the process to obtain an approximation, as close as we wish, to the value for a circle; this ratio is the number π, which is 3.14159 – to quote the first few figures only. This geometrical exercise illustrates the method; so long as there is no limit to the smallness of the subdivisions that we may consider, we can tackle many problems otherwise insoluble.

44

Newton, Laplace, Lagrange, Gauss, Green, Euler, Jacobi – all these great mathematicians thought along these lines. James Clerk Maxwell, thinking in this fashion, predicted the electromagnetic waves later discovered by Hertz and applied so successfully by Oliver Lodge, Marconi and others. Light, heat radiation and radio waves were undoubtedly all one in nature and origin; the continuous nature of the process by which waves were produced seemed unquestionable – as unquestionable as the mathematical methods used to treat of them. Mathematics based on continuous variation is the foundation of the thermodynamical reasoning used by Rayleigh, Jeans and even Wien, in their attempts to explain the way in which the energy of these waves is distributed throughout the spectrum; but none of them, as we have seen, got the answer right. Thermodynamics gave a result in dramatic contrast to experiment. All available energy ought to crowd into the very shortest waves, leaving almost nothing remaining in the longer waves. This is the so-called 'ultra-violet catastrophe' – a melodramatic name for the behaviour, luckily fictitious, of a universe governed by nineteenth-century physics.

From all this, it becomes apparent that the prophecy of an ultra-violet catastrophe is false, not because the argument is wrong, but because error lies in the assumption that the quantities under discussion can be infinitely subdivided. So long as the steps in the calculations are finite in size, all is well; it is when the transition is made to an infinity of infinitesimally small steps that the catastrophe occurs. To use a humble analogy, we may ascend or descend between different levels in a building, not only by climbing the stairs, but also by travelling in the lift. If the lift is properly designed it will move smoothly and continuously, but we can stop it at any height by pushing the emergency button. This is something we cannot do if we use the stairs, where we can stop where we like – but only at the level of one of the stair treads, which are finite and limited in number. This distinction is by no means frivolous; it is much more than the difference between Victorian and modern

45

architecture, between American progress and English anachronisms. It marks a fundamental dichotomy of ideas. In a building, smooth ascent in a lift may be preferable to the labour of climbing the stairs one at a time, but in atomic physics a stepwise progress is essential. We shall see this if we follow Max Planck in his solution of the problem of the distribution of energy in the spectrum.

Planck realized that, empirically, the solution was easy. The two formulae of Rayleigh and of Wien were only limiting cases of a simple formula containing both as extremes, to be used at high and low frequencies respectively. But how was this formula to be justified? In December 1900, he had no answer; but three months later he had the explanation, and this explanation turned the ideas of physics topsy-turvy. The disturbance it caused shattered any complacency into which some physicists had been tempted to retire. For some thirteen years, his ideas, which were unbelievably fruitful, gained ground; until, just before the First World War, Niels Bohr combined them with the ideas Rutherford was putting forward about the structure of the atom. Then, suddenly, the disconnected facts of spectroscopy, patiently accumulated for more than half a century, began to come into focus as a coherent picture.

What were these revolutionary ideas? To revert to the homely metaphor, it was that, on the atomic scale, nature did not permit us to ascend or descend smoothly between different levels of energy. We had naïvely assumed that, in theory, we could always use the lift, when in hard fact we had to climb the stairs, a step at a time. This is a crudely picturesque way of putting the quantum hypothesis, which should be more precisely stated. The first point to make is that on the atomic scale one can distinguish levels or steps of energy, but loitering between them is not permitted. Atoms may gain or lose energy by emission or absorption of radiation, but only in definite and precise amounts, the amount being the gain, or loss, of energy in transition from one step to another. The second is that the frequency of the wave emitted is sharply defined as being the quotient of the change of energy divided by a universal constant, named Planck's constant after the inspired physicist who dared to imagine atomic behaviour so strangely at variance with large-scale happenings. Very quickly, from these postulates, statistical theory can be used to arrive at Planck's formula which is found exactly to describe the experimental results of observation.

This conception of Max Planck's was not at first acceptable, and this is not to be wondered at. But Einstein saw that if such ideas were to be accepted in one field, they should be applicable in others. In 1905, in the same year that he put forward his theory of Relativity, he saw that Planck's ideas explained the puzzling phenomena of photoelectric emission, in which violet or ultra-violet light falling on a metal caused it to lose a negative electrical charge. During the next year or two Einstein applied the ideas of the quantum theory, as Max Planck's hypothesis is known, to the problem of the variation of specific heats with temperature. It was found that the amount of heat required to change the temperature of a body was not constant, but decreased surprisingly rapidly as the temperature was lowered towards the absolute zero of temperature. This was another problem insoluble by classical thermodynamics. Einstein saw that quantum theory, however, would give the result observed. At least it gave an answer so very nearly in agreement with observation, that everyone was convinced that the quantum theory must have within it the seeds of truth, even if the details of its application should need modifying. Peter Debye (1884–) soon produced the necessary modifications. A few years later the science of photo-chemistry was born, when Einstein saw that the quantum theory, applied here, once again yielded a satisfactory explanation of experimental observations.

It will be appreciated that the quantum theory treats radiant energy, not as continuously divisible, but as made up in parcels – very small parcels, but parcels of a definite size – indivisible while in transit from one atom to another, from the atom of origin to the receiving or absorbing atom. The physicist calls these bundles or parcels of energy, photons, or quanta. These indivisible bundles of energy, travelling in straight lines from the point of origin to the point of reception, are strangely like the corpuscles, of which Newton supposed light to consist. Radiation, having all the properties of waves, nevertheless has some of the properties of particles.

Oddly enough, while I was at Bowdoin College, in Maine, preparing to deliver the lectures that constitute this book, I found in the vaults under the chapel on the campus a paper contributed by James Bowdoin to the first volume of the Memoirs of the American Academy of Arts and Sciences of which he was a founder and the first president. The title of the paper, written in 1783, startled me not a little; indeed I think it must make any physicist of 1966 prick up his ears: 'Observations on the waste of matter in the Sun and the Stars occasioned by the constant efflux of light from them.'

Bowdoin starts by discussing an objection that Benjamin Franklin had made in 1768 to the effect that if light were indeed a stream of particles, the reception of even one such particle going at the immense speed at which light was known to travel, would be similar to the impact of a 24-lb ball fired from a cannon. Against this, Bowdoin points out that light corpuscles must be of infinitesimal mass so that their momentum is very small. Then, from the facts that a candle flame is visible at a distance of four miles or more, and that the radius of the pupil of an eye is but about a tenth of an inch, he deduced an upper limit to the size of the light corpuscle. He then argues that the total mass of the emitted corpuscles cannot be greater, and must in fact be considerably less, than the mass of the candle flame, and obtains by simple calculation an upper limit to the mass of a single particle. Small as this is, this mass is not negligible, so that the sun and the stars must be subject to a continual wasting away of their substance as a result of the constant efflux of light from them. He remarks that if the Creator did not wish the sun to be a permanent feature of His creation, this was of no consequence; but that if He wished it

48

to maintain its ability to emit light for great periods of time, this waste of substance must be compensated. He ends by suggesting that the falling into the sun of comets, and other heavenly objects, might be sufficient replenishment.

This anticipation of the modern concept that mass and radiant energy are mutually interconvertible tempts one to speculate on the course of the development of physics. If the ideas put forward by James Bowdoin had gained wide acceptance prior to Thomas Young's demonstration of the wave nature of light in 1800, would the quantum theory have had to wait until its formulation by Max Planck in 1900?

Today none doubts the universal applicability of the quantum laws, but the reasons behind them were not clear for a very long time, not until one of the most remarkable pieces of inspired guesswork was made in 1924. But before this can be appreciated we must look in retrospect at the development of physics after Faraday had discovered the laws of electrolysis, that is to say the quantitative laws of liberation of chemical elements by an electric current.

Soon after Volta in 1800 had invented the electric pile, thus providing the earliest source of a continuous current of electricity, it was found that the passage of electricity through a chemical solution caused decomposition of the dissolved substance, the products of decomposition accumulating at the points of entry and egress of the current. When in 1834 Faraday turned his attention to this phenomenon, his skill as a trained chemist quickly enabled him to establish that the passage of a definite quantity of electricity liberated equally precisely defined quantities of the chemical substances produced. The relationship is exact and inviolable: with any given quantity of a particular chemical element there is invariably associated a certain quantity of electricity, no more and no less.

During the early part of the nineteenth century science, especially chemical science, had gradually become convinced of the atomic nature of matter, that is to say that there is a limit to the size of the particles into which any portion of a chemical

49

element can be subdivided. This limit is the atom. Because there is a quantitative relation between matter and electricity it follows logically that electricity too is atomic in nature. This necessary consequence was strangely slow to be fully accepted; but it was as a result of other experiments started by Michael Faraday on the discharge of electricity through gases, that J. J. Thomson (1856–1940) finally discovered in 1896 the elementary particle of electricity. He was able to show that the luminescent cathode rays in a discharge tube, at first thought to be some kind of electromagnetic waves, were but streams of swiftly moving particles of disembodied electricity. These elementary units became known as electrons, and from then on the properties of the electron, its mass (which is very small), its charge and its behaviour in laboratory apparatus were studied extensively. In 1911 Ernest Rutherford put forward the guess that electrons play the same role in the atom that the planets do in the solar system, and in 1913 Niels Bohr (1885–1962) with a brilliant flash of inspiration saw how to apply the quantum theory to such a model of the atom. He was abundantly justified, for he obtained from his equations a formula completely describing the spectrum of hydrogen, and of helium, both puzzles of long standing. But though the quantum theory once again gave the right answer, the reasons were still hidden in obscurity, and remained so for more than a decade. The solution came with a mystical synthesis of the two opposite concepts – a wave and a corpuscle – that have divided physics for so long.

Natural philosophers have always been fascinated by the idea of elementary particles. Democritus the Greek had his atoms; Newton had his corpuscles of light, and even suggested still subtler swiftly moving corpuscles pervading all space which by their impact on matter exerted the forces of gravity between the heavenly bodies and, indeed, between any two material objects. Franklin entertained vague speculations concerning the nature of the electric fluid and wondered if in its ultimate nature it were not corpuscular. But there have always been sceptics among the scientists. As late as this century Ernst Mach still denied any reality to chemical atoms, maintaining that they were merely convenient figments of imagination for facilitating chemical calculations. Brownian motion, that violent and perpetual agitation of any freely suspended small particles which may be observed under a microscope, or better, an ultra-microscope, demonstrated to all but the most obstinate disbeliever the reality of the kinetic theory of atoms and molecules of matter. But what of the newly postulated corpuscles of electricity and of energy, the electron and the quantum? Although at the outset cathode rays had been thought to be some kind of waves the electron that finally emerged was clearly a particle. Equally clearly light and X-rays both appeared to be waves, the quantum of energy essential for accurate calculation having more the air of a ledger entry in the accounts than of a concrete entity.

In 1923 Arthur H. Compton (1892–1962) in Chicago, studying the scattering of X-rays, found, to put the matter picturesquely though somewhat crudely, that he could play a kind of billiards with photons and electrons. (What Newton called a *corpuscle*, what Bowdoin called a *particle*, we today call a *photon*. It is a quantum of radiant energy.) Compton found that the laws of collision held good in his experiments, although there the red ball was an electron, and the cue ball a photon. For this remarkable discovery he was awarded a Nobel prize. Its importance lay in the demonstration that both the electron and the photon have similar particle-like properties, of which the most significant is their common ability to possess, and to exchange, definite amounts of energy and of momentum: in fact, as I have said, to behave very much like billiard balls. But within a year the wheel was to come full circle, and another scientist, with almost mystical insight, was to perceive in the motion of particles the familiar pattern of waves.

In 1924 the Duc Louis de Broglie (1892–) submitted his thesis for a degree, in which he suggested that if waves had some of the properties of particles, perhaps particles had some of the properties of waves. From the equations of relativity he showed

51

that this hypothesis would give a rational explanation of the rules of quantum theory. What did the degree examiners think of de Broglie's thesis? Was it the inspiration of genius or the wild fantasy of a fanatic? Whatever their thoughts, the Duc received his degree, the thesis was published, and wave mechanics was born. Erwin Schrödinger (1887–1961) saw that this was an idea to which the mathematics of wave motion could be immediately applied; and the wave equation, governing motion of atomic and sub-atomic particles, is today known by his name. The mechanics applicable to small-scale phenomena is, in fact, the mechanics of waves and not the mechanics of particles.

By one of those notable coincidences of which the history of science is full, another physicist, Werner Heisenberg (1901–), who had recently joined Max Born at Göttingen, was at that very time engaged in attacking the problems posed by the quantum theory of spectra. His plan was simple – to formulate a theory in which only observables should occur; but this sublime simplicity led to surprising mathematical complexity. Heisenberg found himself having to develop rules for operating with matrices, as the square arrangements of numbers with which he had to deal were called; at the time, he was unaware that matrices had already been the subject of exhaustive study by mathematicians before him. The existing quantum theories of Bohr and Sommerfeld explicitly made use of the concept that electrons had defined velocities in orbits of specified sizes and shapes, in spite of the fact that these were unobservable. Heisenberg's theory was far superior to this, and it avoided criticism, since he abjured concepts of unobservables. But his method was difficult, and the simpler wave-mechanics of Schrödinger gave equally good results. It was shown, moreover, that the two methods, so dissimilar in approach, were intrinsically the same. Heisenberg's theory contained a new principle of fundamental importance – the uncertainty, or indeterminacy principle. It is a characteristic of a wave that it spreads over an ill-defined area. It had been thought of a particle that it had a precise location in space. Neither statement is true without qualification. It is possible to define a wave so as to restrict it to a small region of space, but only at the cost of giving it a considerable spread of frequencies. It is impossible to know precisely both the location of the wave and its frequency. The more closely we draw the confines of the wave at the present instant, the less certain shall we be of its position in the future.

We are faced with a similar dilemma if we try to locate a particle. To observe it we must illuminate it. Unfortunately, the impact of the light gives the particle a jolt of undetermined magnitude, so that the very process of locating the particle precludes us from measuring with precision its present velocity or predicting its future position. The process of observation itself alters the course of events in an unpredictable manner. The more accurately one determines the present, the less accurately can one foretell the future.

This is an astonishing state of affairs quite unlike anything Newton or Laplace could have envisaged. It indicates a deep-seated characteristic of the fabric of the universe. It is in stark contradiction to the Victorian concept of physics in which there was no theoretical limit to the process of refining the accuracy with which a physicist could hope to make measurements of the observable world. Twentieth-century theory says bluntly that there is a limit of precision beyond which one cannot go, and that this limit is set, not by unavoidable experimental error, but by the nature of the very stuff of which the world is made. In the final analysis we find the universe to be composed of energy, manifested in either of two forms – of matter or of radiation; but as both alike are governed by quantum rules, the principle of indeterminacy is the ultimate law.

It should be added, that, although to present-day physics indeterminacy seems inevitable and fundamental, it is of importance only in affairs of atomic dimensions or less. In everyday human life it is hidden, obscured by the immense weight of numbers involved in the atomic composition of even the smallest portions of matter with which we are normally concerned.

There is nothing so uncertain as one man's tenure of life, nothing more certain than the statistical tables of expectation of life of the policy-holders of a large insurance company. The inequalities of chance, so evident in the life of an individual, are ironed out when the lives of many individuals are considered; so that if the numbers involved be large enough, chance uncertainty is replaced by statistical certainty. Because in everyday life the numbers of atoms concerned in any event are immense, the statistical argument applies with even greater force, and we can go about our daily business unperturbed by the impact of quantum theory.

There is nevertheless a new look about fundamental concepts which we cannot ignore. The universe is no longer the deterministic machine Laplace imagined it to be. In the finer details of its working we must admit an inherent element of chance. This admission has opened a happy hunting ground to philosophers as well as physicists; even theologians have joined in the chase, though with dubious success. The entire structure of scientific thought has been subjected to minute scrutiny. Even the concept of causality has come under suspicion – a cloud from which it has not entirely emerged.

Lest it should seem that I have followed abstract arguments into realms far removed from experimental science, I will end by recalling the practical outcome of this outstanding example of inspired imaginative guesswork. After de Broglie had drawn the parallel between electrons and photons, suggesting that both had wave-like properties, two experiments, one more or less accidental, the other deliberate, provided quantitative confirmation. The first was by two investigators in the Bell Telephone Laboratories in U.S.A., Davisson (1881–1959) and Germer who, as the result of a mishap which caused their nickel electrode to recrystallize as a single crystal, discovered that a crystal reflected electrons in just the way that one would expect waves to be reflected. The second was by George Paget Thomson (1892–), son of J. J. Thomson the discoverer of the electron. G. P. Thomson thought it should be possible to test

54

de Broglie's hypothesis by firing a beam of electrons through a thin metal foil; this he did, and obtained a diffraction pattern exactly as wave theory predicted. de Broglie's guess was right; his shot in the twilight had hit the bullseye!

Applied physics uses electrons in a variety of devices: in our radio and television, in our telephones and tape-recorders, to name but a few of the more popular. Both industry and medicine accelerate electrons to very high speeds in order to generate penetrating X-rays which may be used for detection of flaws and cracks in metal forgings, and for deep therapy of cancerous growths in the human body. In all these applications it is generally sufficient to think of the electron as behaving like a particle. In the electron microscope, which is widely used to examine structures too fine to be accessible to optical instruments, we approach the point of transition at which either the wave picture or the particle aspect of the electron seem equally valid. The wave-like properties are the more important in research laboratories where diffraction of electrons is a standard technique, not to test the wave-nature of the electron, but to make use of it to investigate the crystalline structure of the diffracting substance.

In all this, with what are we dealing? With waves or particles? With matter or radiation? It all seems to depend on how one arranges the experiment. Seek for the properties of particles, you find them; look for the evidence of waves and it is there. What you cannot do, at one and the same time, by the same experiment, is to get both sets of evidence together. As one physicist put it, on Mondays, Wednesdays and Fridays one has to think about waves; on Tuesdays, Thursdays and Saturdays about particles; on Sundays one just prays. This flippant aphorism has a core of serious meaning!

Scientists are not always solemn, and flippancy may be but a cloak for inner reverence. The physicist, who finds the objects of his search growing smaller and more tenuous the deeper he probes into the secrets of nature, experiences an elation of spirit as he ponders the mysteries revealed, that can perhaps be matched only by the wonder an astronomer feels at the vast and awful depths of space, as he counts some tiny fraction of the innumerable stars, or submits to a celestial census a crowd of galaxies clustering in a corner of the heavens. The spirit of wonder, said Aristotle, first led men to study natural philosophy. Maxwell's earliest memory was of lying on the grass, looking at the sky, and *wondering*. Einstein said that 'whoever is devoid of the capacity to wonder, who can remain unmoved, whoever cannot contemplate or know the deep shudder of the soul in enchantment, might just as well be dead for he has already closed his eyes on life'. Arthur Koestler, discussing creative activity, quotes these sayings and concludes that the common source of mysticism, of science and of art is an 'oceanic feeling of wonder'. *

* Koestler, A., *The Act of Creation*. Hutchinson, London, 1964, p. 258.

Chapter 4

WHIRLIGIGS AND TUNNELS

> Those who refuse to go beyond fact rarely get as far as fact; anyone who has studied the history of science knows that almost every step has been made . . . by the invention of an hypothesis which, though verifiable, often had little foundation to start with.
>
> *Thomas Henry Huxley*

In this final chapter, I shall consider some of the guesses which have been made concerning the ultimate constitution of matter. Most of these have been bold and imaginative. Many have flown in the teeth of accepted beliefs, and have contradicted well-tried principles known to hold in large-scale matters of everyday life, and unquestioningly accepted to be of universal validity. Having already shown how the study of radiation led to the quantum hypothesis, and this in turn to the idea that matter had a wave-like nature, I shall now relate how the study of radio-activity has resulted in the nuclear picture of the atom. This is perhaps the crowning triumph of scientific imagination; and it is the more tragic that so brilliant an achievement is marred by such sinister shadows. We all know how the technical application of nuclear discoveries led, with pitiful consequences, to the liberation of primaeval energy locked in the nucleus since countless ages, and has resulted in the momentary reproduction on earth (on the comparatively small scale of the hydrogen bomb) of processes by which energy is continuously liberated in the deep interior of the sun and the stars. But before we approach the study of the inner nucleus of the atom we must recall the steps by which the constitution of the outer layers of the atom was determined.

The discovery of the elementary particle of electricity was made by John Joseph Thomson; but as we have seen, the origin of this discovery lay in Michael Faraday's measurements of the decomposition of salts in electrolysis.* Helmholtz (1821–94), in his oration in memory of Faraday, observed how Faraday's discovery that with a given mass of any substance a precisely defined quantity of electricity is invariably associated led, when taken in conjunction with Dalton's atomic hypothesis, to the concept of indivisible elementary electrical charges. Johnson Stoney called these elementary charges *electrons*, and the name stuck, although they had not then been detected. A series of experiments on the passage of electricity through gases, started by Faraday and culminating in Sir William Crookes's (1832–1919) observations of cathode rays, made it probable that matter itself was composed, in part, of negative electricity. Some years later, in 1896, the free negatively-charged electrical particle was identified in the gaseous discharge tube, and its properties were measured. It then became profitable to speculate on the origin of this negatively-charged electron, and its function within the atom from whence it came. Because its properties were independent of the metal of the electrodes and of the gas in the discharge tube, it was clearly a universal constituent of matter. It was surprisingly small: some two thousand weighed no more than a single atom of hydrogen, the lightest atom there is. As Helmholtz had foreseen, its electrical charge was found to be equal in magnitude to that carried by atoms in electrolytic solutions.

There was no experimental evidence to indicate its diameter, but physicists surmised that its small mass was indicative of small size. Calculations made on the assumption that it owed its mass entirely to its electrical charge suggested that its diameter was some 10,000 times less than the diameter of an atom. The size of atoms was already known approximately from observations on gases, and it became a matter of interest to imagine what kind of relation existed between the electron

* See p. 49.

and the rest of the atom. J. J. Thomson, pushing his researches further, found positively-charged particles in the rays in an electrical discharge tube; these particles were found to have masses equal to the masses of the atoms of the gas in the tube, and to have electrical charges which, though of positive sign, were equal in magnitude to the charge on the electron, or else were small multiples of that charge. The violence of the electrical discharge had been able to rupture some of the gas atoms, knocking away negatively charged electrons and leaving the residues positively charged. A century and a half earlier Benjamin Franklin had stated that withdrawal of positive electricity from a body left it negatively charged. What Franklin had seen in his study and on the vast scale of the heavens, Thomson perceived on the minute scale of the atom, the only difference being the trivial reversal of signs.

From his experiments Thomson concluded correctly that an atom consisted of a heavy part, carrying nearly all the mass and having a positive charge, sufficient negative electrons being attached to this to render the whole atom electrically neutral. The question was how many electrons were involved? Were the electrons attached to the outside of the atom rather like the poppy seeds on a continental bread roll? Some of the electrons at any rate were easily detachable. The electrostatic force of attraction between each negatively-charged electron and the positively charged remainder of the atom, together with the forces of mutual repulsion between the negative electrons, might well be sufficient to account for the stability of the whole structure. Chemical elements were known to show powers of attachment to each other, suggesting that stable configurations of eight electrons might account for the observed laws of chemical combination. This hypothesis was ingenious but not mechanically satisfactory. J. J. Thomson modified it by imagining that the atom resembled a currant bun in which the electrons were embedded in the atom like the currants in the bun. This idea gave a better chance of explaining the periodic table of the chemical elements, but it made it harder to see how the

59

embedded electrons could be as easily removed as observation showed them to be.

In the first decade of this century Ernest Rutherford, who had started his study of science by working with wireless waves, became interested in the remarkable properties of radium. This element had recently been isolated by the Curies, and was known to emit strange and puzzling radiations which caused a gold leaf electroscope to lose its electrical charge very quickly. Rutherford discovered these radiations to be of three different types, which he named α, β, and γ rays. The latter were seen to be like X-rays, or ultra-violet light; the β-rays were found to be very swiftly-moving electrons; but the α-rays were altogether new. Rutherford found that they were exceedingly energetic; and though they could penetrate matter for only a short distance, they did a tremendous amount of damage in their path, knocking electrons out of the atoms they met. He found them to have a mass equal to that of an atom of helium, viz: four times that of a hydrogen atom, and to have an electrical charge equal in magnitude to that of two electrons, but of positive sign. He collected spent α-rays, and obtained a minute quantity of a gas which, when excited in an electrical discharge tube, gave the spectrum of helium.* In fact the α-particle was simply a helium atom that had lost two electrons. Why or how such a particle came to be shot out of an atom of radium was a mystery – but it was a marvellous gift of nature to the experimental physicist. Radium is the source of the most energetic missiles then known to man. The damage a missile can do may be estimated if its velocity and mass be known. The ratio of its kinetic energy to its mass gives a graphic indication of the relative power of destruction a missile has by virtue of its speed alone. For example, if the energy-to-mass ratio of an aeroplane just breaking the sound barrier as it travels at about 300 yards a second be taken as our unit of comparison, then the energy-to-mass ratio of a rifle bullet is about four times; that of a satellite, orbiting the earth at about four miles a second, a

* 1909.

thousand times; and that of an α-particle is ten thousand million times, greater. An α-particle leaves its parent atom at a speed initially about ten million yards a second. It is not surprising that it does much damage. That it travels such a very small distance, only an inch or two in ordinary air, is due to the very large number of collisions it makes with the atoms of air in its path, of which there are many millions of millions of millions.

Realizing that he had at his command atomic artillery of stupendous power, incredibly energetic atomic missiles, Rutherford set his students to work on the numerous atomic firing-ranges into which he transformed his laboratory. The results were much as might have been expected, until in 1911 events were observed so astounding and so significant that they must be described in Rutherford's own words. He was engaged in finding by how much α-particles could be deflected, before collisions with the numerous atoms of matter brought them to a stop. He found, very occasionally, that an α-particle would rebound backwards from the target. 'It was as astonishing,' he said, 'as if an artilleryman firing armour-piercing shells at heavy armour plate, found that sometimes a shell would rebound after hitting merely a sheet of paper.' The event was indisputably observed, but on any theory of statistics it was too improbable to be credible. He could only conclude that the atom could not possibly be the diffuse structure that had been supposed. Sir Ernest Rutherford's mathematics was never his strongest point, but he knew his Newtonian mechanics. The path of a planet or a comet wheeling round the sun must be, as Kepler found, one of the well-known curves that mathematicians call conic sections. This must also be true of an α-particle approaching an atom. In this case, the forces involved must be electrical instead of gravitational, but apart from that, the difference is but one of scale, and it is a matter of simple calculation to work out the distance of nearest approach of the two – the α-particle and the atom. The answer was staggering. It was a distance tens of thousands of times smaller than the known

61

diameter of the atom. The α-particle must have been able to penetrate deep into the core of the atom, there to encounter the main mass which must be concentrated in a volume less than a billionth part of the whole. The atom must, in fact, be largely empty space. Rutherford, who resembled Michael Faraday in the vividness of his imagination, saw that the only picture which could possibly fit the facts was one in which the atom was like the solar system, with a heavy central nucleus playing the part of the sun, the much lighter electrons circling round it like so many planets, and the gravitational forces of attraction replaced by the electric forces of attraction between the positively-charged nucleus and the negatively-charged electrons.

William Blake saw 'the world in a grain of sand, and a heaven in a wild flower'. He held 'Infinity in the palm of [his] hand, and eternity in an hour'. But to see the solar system in the atom is surely a feat of imagination of equal brilliance. The scale-ratio of one to the other is some thousand million million million to one. Man is curiously poised between two extremes, the infinitely large and the infinitely small. The contrast has inspired many, among them Blaise Pascal (1623–62), mathematician, physicist and man of God. Meditating on the Infinite he asks us to contemplate a puny mite, saying of even its smallest part that he would depict therein not merely a world like our own, but an entire universe contracted within the confines of that tiny microcosm. Therein he could descry an infinity of worlds, each with its firmament, its planets, its earth, its animals and even its mites; in these mites again the whole repeats, and so and on in an endlessly diminishing chain, till he is lost in wonder at marvels so minute but no less amazing than those of gigantic size. It needs, he says, no less capacity for attaining the Nothing than the All. Infinite capacity is required for both.*

To return to Rutherford's nuclear atom, the idea was beset

* Pascal, Blaise, *Pensées*: 'Sur la disproportion de l'homme': 'Les deux infinis' (paraphrased by the author). See also W. F. Trotter's translation (Dent), and H. F. Stewart's translation (Panther Books, New York, 1950).

with difficulties, not the least of which concerned the permanency of such a system. To understand the problem of its stability, let us think of water beetles, those little aquatic insects one sometimes sees on the surface of quiet ponds, whirling round and round in small circles. These tiny creatures ruffle the water, sending out ripples which radiate away in all directions. After a while the beetle stops. The source of energy exhausted, the ripples cease. We see much the same thing if a small boy stirs the water violently with a stick, sending larger waves all over the pond; but he too stops when he is tired. It is the same with a circulating electric charge. The electro-magnetic waves it generates we recognize as radio waves, and their maintenance requires a steady supply of energy. A planetary electron circling round the nucleus of an atom must similarly radiate energy, and in so doing it must – like a satellite whirling round the earth and losing energy to the atmosphere – spiral inwards. The negatively-charged electron must ultimately fall into the positively-charged nucleus, so that the atom must, apparently, annihilate itself. Yet the most obvious feature of matter is its permanence, so clearly atoms do not collapse and vanish. Equally obviously, atoms do not continuously radiate electromagnetic waves, of light, or indeed of any other form, except when stimulated to do so by the ambient conditions of the moment. It looked, therefore, as if Planck's quantum postulates should be applied: there must be immensely long periods of quiescence during which atoms do not radiate. Atomic spectra had always been perplexing. Physicists were sure that the key to atomic structure would be found when the complicated pattern of frequencies was unravelled. Even simple atoms emit light of many different frequencies, and these are all sharply defined. An atom of hydrogen is the simplest atom of all and can contain only a central positively-charged nucleus and a single negatively-charged planetary electron. This simple structure should, on classical laws, radiate only at one frequency. Like the boy stirring the water with a stick, or the water beetle spinning on the surface, the radiated waves have the frequency of the

63

rotation; and like the orbiting satellite losing energy as it goes, the circling electron must rotate ever faster and faster as it spirals towards the centre. The light it emits must spread continuously through the whole spectrum, from red to blue, into the ultra-violet and beyond to the shortest waves of all. But in fact the light from a hydrogen atom contains only a finite number of sharply-defined frequencies, arranged according to arithmetical rules, simple, but totally inexplicable.

In 1913 Niels Bohr, who had been working in Rutherford's laboratory, was pondering on the problem of these frequencies. The quantum theory of energy had, indeed, been applied successfully in many other fields: by Planck himself to temperature radiation; by Einstein and Debye to specific heats; by Einstein to photoelectricity and photochemistry. But Bohr realized that a naïve application of the theory of quantization of energy would not serve. If quantum theory were to succeed again it must be used differently. Until then it had not been necessary to distinguish between energy and a related concept known to mechanics as *action*. But for a rotating system such as Rutherford conceived the atom to be, the distinction was necessary. The principles of quantum theory when applied not to energy, but to *action* (which in this case is the angular momentum of the electron), immediately gave Niels Bohr the correct formula for the frequencies of the known spectral lines of hydrogen. Indeed, it also correctly predicted other series of lines, then unknown but subsequently observed, in the ultra-violet and infra-red. Niels Bohr would have been justified in exulting in prose as colourful and ecstatic as Johann Kepler's; but unfortunately the twentieth century is too self-consciously sober and restrained.

Sommerfeld took up the work and found that the introduction of Kepler's laws of planetary motion provided almost more startling corroboration of the theory. On the same principles as those obtaining in celestial mechanics, the orbits of the electrons round the atomic nucleus must in general be ellipses. Relativity theory applied to these orbits predicted a precession,* similar to the precession observed in the orbit of the planet Mercury round the sun, to which I have already referred. This precession provided a fine structure to the spectral lines precisely in accordance with observation. Triumph could scarcely be more complete. And yet there was still no suggestion of the reasons underlying the apparently arbitrary demands of the quantum theory. Postulates once correctly made, results followed; but the reasons for the postulates were completely obscure.

In the previous chapter I mentioned the almost mystical guess of the Duc de Broglie, to whom it seemed rational to think that if waves could behave like particles, particles might behave like waves. If this were so, then it followed that, if the electron circling the nucleus were of the nature of a wave, this wave could represent a stable condition, *only* if its wavelength were precisely right to fit exactly into the length of the path. The perimeter of the orbit must be an integral number of times the wavelength, otherwise there could be no fit, no coincidence, but rather complete confusion. It follows from this that only certain energy-states of the atomic system are permissible, only certain orbits are allowed, just as quantum theory demands; the quantum theory, instead of being merely an ingenious method of predicting the correct answers, now becomes a rational system, reasonable and inevitable, elegant and satisfying. The methods of wave-mechanics which Erwin Schrödinger developed from de Broglie's guess, today not only provide an explanation of extra-nuclear structure and behaviour, but also help to solve some of the problems of the inner structure of the nucleus itself.

When the study of nuclear physics was in its infancy, Rutherford had found that one of the characteristics of α-particles was the constancy of the energy with which they were ejected from the parent radioactive atoms. Any one α-particle was shot from the parent nucleus as the result of an entirely unpredictable explosion; but no matter when this happened, all

* See p. 37.

α-particles had the same energy. Yet careful measurement showed that this was far less than would be needful for the α-particle to re-enter the nucleus. How was it able to escape from imprisonment within the nucleus, if its store of energy was too little for it to surmount the prison walls? This was a puzzle, until Gamow (1904–) saw that wave-mechanics provided the solution to the paradox. Like the electron, an α-particle has a dual nature. Look at it in one light, and it seems like a minute high-speed cannon ball; look at it in another and it seems like a fine-textured wave. Now waves can leak through barriers impenetrable to particles. Sound waves, for instance, pass through walls. Luckily for those who live in flats their loudness and vigour are considerably diminished in the process. But to some extent, through they go, and to this extent α-particles resemble them. α-particles do not have to climb the ramparts, but in the true tradition of escape-stories, they tunnel through them. Just as in escape-stories, they are not invariably successful; but success comes more easily and more often the thinner the ramparts. It little avails the commandant of the fortress to raise the height of the walls, but he more easily frustrates the efforts of his prisoners by making the walls thicker, thus forcing the fugitives to dig longer tunnels. This is not merely a picturesque way of describing the situation; it parallels exactly the state of an α-particle imprisoned in the nucleus; even the details are in quantitative agreement with observation.

This is not all. There were other vital clues to nuclear structure to be found in the mathematics of the quantum theory. Paul Adrien Maurice Dirac (1902–), an engineer from Bristol who turned mathematical physicist, worked out a fully relativistic theory of the electron, and noticed that his equations could be interpreted in a remarkable manner. He thought that all energy-states of electrons defined by his equations should be equally permissible, from which it followed that even a vacuum must be represented as teeming with electrons, though all having negative energy. If from this sea of electrons, a single one were to leap to a state of positive energy, this would mean the

66

appearance of a negatively charged electron, but the hole it left behind would appear like an electron of positive charge. This is only Benjamin Franklin's doctrine over again, but in far more sophisticated guise. Exciting as the idea was, it seemed to be illusory, since positive electrons were unknown. Very regretfully physicists concluded that this mathematical curiosity was no more than a trick of the equations, having no particular relevance to the world of material particles.

Two years later, however, an American, Carl David Anderson (1905–), and Patrick Maynard Stuart Blackett, then professor at Imperial College, London, simultaneously observed and identified particles having the same small mass as an electron, but carrying a positive charge instead of a negative one. This was the first of a sequence of similar discoveries. The positive electron (called the positron), and the negative electron, have all their properties, except one, the same: they differ only in the sign of their electric charge. They are the first examples of two types of material particle of which others have since been discovered. It is now believed that all material particles can exist in two such forms, and it has consequently become the habit to speak of *matter* and *anti-matter*. If the two forms come together they mutually annihilate one another with very great evolution of energy released in the form of radiation; that is to say, particles of matter become transformed into electromagnetic waves. The reverse process also has been observed; that is, very energetic γ-rays may become converted into two particles, a positron and an electron, the one a particle of matter and the other of anti-matter, just as Dirac had supposed.

In 1932, the same year that the positron was discovered almost by chance, another of Rutherford's pupils, James Chadwick (1891–), suggested that some very puzzling behaviour, observed as a result of bombarding beryllium with α-particles, could be simply explained by postulating the existence of a new particle. This new particle was presumed to have a mass similar to that of the nucleus of an atom of hydrogen, the proton, but to be electrically neutral; that is to say, it carried no electrical charge. It was suggested that the particle, called a neutron, was a constituent of the nucleus of every atom, and that it appeared as a result of being knocked out by a direct hit by the atomic missile. It will be seen that a swiftly moving massive particle, carrying no electrical charge, must travel a long way in matter before being stopped. Having no charge, it is surrounded by no electrical field and has no means of interacting with the electrical atmospheres of the atoms it encounters, and it can do no damage on its way. It can be stopped only by a direct hit on a nucleus. Only then, at the end of its flight, can it be recognized by the nuclear disintegration resulting from the direct hit. This was precisely what had been observed.

An old hypothesis of Prout (1785–1850) put forward in 1815 was now seen to be vindicated after nearly 120 years. Prout, noting that the masses of the atoms of all chemical elements were very nearly whole-number multiples of the mass of an atom of hydrogen, had supposed that in fact all other atoms were composed of atoms of hydrogen. This guess had not received support, because no one could either decompose elements into hydrogen, or combine hydrogen atoms to form atoms of other elements. But as soon as Chadwick discovered the neutron, a modification of Prout's hypothesis made good sense. The nuclei of all atoms were to be thought of as composed of neutrons and protons, in correct proportion (in equal, or nearly equal numbers) to give the required mass and positive electrical charge.

This simplification of atomic theory, this revival of an early guess, this development arising from modern studies of radioactivity, has led to far-reaching consequences. Among other things, the alchemist's dream of transmutation of the elements has come true. Not perhaps in quite the way he had hoped to make noble metals, especially gold, from baser ones, but in a manner scientifically far more valuable. For instance, gold when subjected to bombardment by neutrons turns into a pure form of mercury containing atoms of only a single species, unlike naturally occurring mercury, which has atoms of many different species inseparable by chemical means. A new art has come into being, the transmutation of elements by irradiation with neutrons in nuclear reactors, the so-called atomic piles, which generate neutrons in vast numbers. As most of the products of transmutation are radioactive, their uses in industry, as well as in pure research, are many.

Many radioactive transformations take place with ejection of β-particles. These are swiftly-moving electrons, but they escape with widely varying energies, and this sets the physicist an intractable problem of accountancy. The β-particles all start with the same energy, like travellers all starting with the same sum of money. But no sooner have they started than some are still flush with money, others are almost penniless. What has happened to the money they have lost? Has it been stolen? What has happened to the energy the β-particle had from its nuclear bank? It is the theme-song of the physicist that energy may frequently change its appearance, but there is a constant refrain that the total energy is strictly conserved. To admit that energy might just appear and disappear, like Banquo's ghost, would be to lose hold in this shifting world of phenomena, and risk being swept into the terrors of a nightmare storm. A few physicists had stoically braced themselves to face just such an intellectual horror, when the imagination of two men, Wolfgang Pauli (1900–58) and Enrico Fermi (1901–54), came to the rescue. They surmised that, if the books would not balance, a thief must be at work. A third particle must be involved, a neutrino, and this, cloaked in invisibility, must have carried off the missing energy. The neutrino, it was suggested, is impossible to find, for it has neither electrical charge nor mass. For twenty years it has hidden, securely invisible in this nihilistic cloak, in spite of the fact that a nuclear reactor of even moderate size emits neutrinos in such gigantic numbers that the flux of energy carried off into outer space, could it be caught, would be enough to light a whole town. However, like any other thief, a neutrino occasionally makes a false move. It is like a thief who is never caught, but whose existence is betrayed by the demeanour of a bystander. In this atomic adventure-story it happens once in a while that a proton is so startled that it turns into a neutron and a positron. The positron can be caught, so the presence of the neutrino may be inferred.

The concept of the nuclear atom, the discovery of the neutron, and the guess that neutrons and protons together compose the nucleus, have brought the physicist far along the road to which the search for material knowledge first drew his steps. Wave mechanics, a method of describing the behaviour of particles, gave him an explanation of some of the rules he observed to hold among the electrons circling in the outer reaches of the atom, and it gave him a method of describing some of the properties of particles composing the nucleus. But any rational explanation of the forces binding these particles together was missing, until in 1935 a Japanese scientist, Yukawa (1907–), drew a parallel between the way positively-charged nuclei and negatively-charged electrons combine to form atoms, and the way in which protons and neutrons combine to form nuclei. The field of attraction between positive and negative charges may be thought of as the result of a continual exchange between them of a quantum of electromagnetic energy. Small as they are, electrons are too large and diffuse to be contained within the far smaller nucleus; but Yukawa imagined another kind of charged particle, called a meson, which linked the protons and neutrons together by being exchanged between them. Such a particle, if electrically charged, must have a mass intermediate between that of the electron and that of the proton. In 1936, only a year after Yukawa's suggestion, the first observation of such intermediate type of particle was made by C. D. Anderson, the same man who three years earlier had discovered the positron. Since then the properties of mesons have been the subject of intensive study. It has been found that they may be produced as a result of bombarding atomic nuclei with high-speed missiles, such as hydrogen nuclei that have been given relatively enormous energies by accelerating them in one of the modern great machines for nuclear research. These machines

70

are able to give particles an energy which, reckoned as energy per unit mass, is many hundreds of millions of millions of times greater than the energy per unit mass of a rifle bullet. The damage these particles do when they collide with an atomic nucleus is such that the nucleus disintegrates and the mesons released in this nuclear catastrophe can be studied. Thus nuclear physicists learn about the composition and stability of the innermost citadel of the atom. But their results, which are the fruits of fiery yet controlled imagination of many in a long line of researchers, tax our powers of appreciation.

Remarkable things are happening in physics, so that one wonders where the dividing line between sober theory and wild phantasy can be drawn, if indeed there is such a division. Experimental physics is progressing by proliferation of particles; by postulating that atoms – those hard, massy impenetrable atoms of Democritus, who conceived them as being eternal and indestructible – not only have a microstructure like miniature solar systems; but that the central core itself is composed of parts in close combination, cemented together by exchange between them of still smaller particles. Disintegration of this central core releases a crop of these fundamental particles, most of which have no permanent existence, but which dissolve and fade and change into others, like the insubstantial shades of an esoteric ghost story.

To match these happenings in the laboratory, theoretical physics is becoming dominated by the concepts of number and symmetry to a degree that recalls sixteenth-century thought. There is an almost mystical element in the modern attitude. There is reliance on abstract principles of symmetry that would arouse Kepler's enthusiasm. It seems that these are not flights of mere fancy, but have a surprisingly effective correspondence with experimental work. Considerations of symmetry recently demanded the existence of ten groups of fundamental particles of which only nine were known. Within weeks of this theoretical pronouncement, the missing particle – the omega-minus – was found. What is to come? Physicists are already discussing the next level of discovery, and the sub-particles at this level have been named even before they have been observed. Somewhat humorously, they are called *quarks* – not snarks; but the hunting of the quark is in full cry. And when the quark is found, will it too disappear – as a kind of *boojum* perhaps?

We can be sure only that the adventure of physics will go on so long as the spirit of curiosity and speculation is dear to the human mind. It is certain that at least some of the ideas prevalent today will be modified or even superseded tomorrow, but it is likely that many will survive as the foundations from which new, as yet undreamed of, flights of imagination may be launched.

BIOGRAPHICAL NOTES

ADAMS, John Couch (1819–92), was born at Laneast, Cornwall, on 5 June, and entered St John's College, Cambridge, where in 1842 he was Smith's prizeman and senior wrangler. In the previous year he noted in his diary that he intended to solve the puzzle of the erratic motion of the planet Uranus as soon as he had taken his degree. He kept this resolve and by 1845 had sent his first solution to Challis at Cambridge, a solution which was so nearly correct that, had a search then been instituted, the discovery of the planet Neptune would have been made immediately instead of having to await Leverrier's prediction more than a year later. Adams was appointed to a professorship at St Andrews, Scotland in 1858, but returned next year to become Lowndean professor at Cambridge where, after two years, he succeeded Challis as director of the Observatory. Besides his youthful success in predicting exactly the position of a hitherto unknown planet, he made significant discoveries in other fields, including the motions of the moon and the Leonids (shooting stars which recur each November), and terrestrial magnetism.

ANDERSON, Carl David (1905–), was born in New York on 3 September. He was educated at Los Angeles Polytechnical High School and the Californian Institute of Technology whence he graduated with the highest honours and where in 1932 he observed in a cloud chamber tracks left by positive electrons. The existence of such positively charged particles had been predicted in 1930 by Dirac; in England, Blackett and Occhialini, who had set themselves to find them, discovered them shortly after Anderson. For his priority in making this important contribution to our knowledge of fundamental particles Anderson received the Nobel prize in 1936. Blackett's services to physics were subsequently recognized when he was given the Nobel award for 1948. Since 1939 Anderson has been professor at the Californian Institute of Technology.

ARAGO, Dominique François Jean (1786–1853), was born at Estragel on 26 February and was educated at Perpignan at the École Polytechnique in Paris. Early in his professional life he was in Spain assisting Jean Baptiste Biot to measure the exact length of a degree of latitude when he was captured during the Spanish hostilities with France and, though he escaped in a ship, he was recaptured and kept prisoner for three years. On his return, aged twenty-three, he was elected to the Académie des Sciences and made professor of geometry at the École Polytechnique. He was the first to demonstrate the magnetic action of a current-carrying solenoid and the influence of a rotating magnet on a non-magnetic conducting metal disc. But his greatest contributions to science were in the field of optics in which he worked closely with Fresnel. Together they devised a method of performing the crucial experiment that was to decide between the rival corpuscular and wave theories of light, an experiment which Arago was unable to complete by reason of a sudden failure of his eyesight, but which Foucault carried out in 1850, and found that light travelled faster in air than in water.

ARISTOTLE (384–322 B.C.), was born at Stagira and went to Athens in 367 B.C. where he was, for thirty years, a member of Plato's academy. In 343 he became tutor to Alexander at Pella, but when nine years later Alexander set out to conquer Asia, he returned to Athens and founded his own school. In 323 he was accused of impiety and he retired to Chalcis, where he died. He seems to have been of a kindly and affectionate nature with indomitable energy and a breadth of interest that can truly be called encyclopaedic. H. G. Lewes said of him that his vast intellect gave the impulse to philosophy, but that in the discovery of positive truths the results of his labours were insignificant when not erroneous. In spite of the justice of this assessment we must pay tribute nevertheless to Aristotle for his advocacy of reason and observation against myth and superstition; his aim was to scrutinize and record all events in human and natural history so that knowledge might be built upon firm foundations. In this he may be considered to be the father of scientific method.

BACON, Francis, 1st Baron Verulam and Viscount St Alban (1561–1626), was born in London on 22 January, the son of Sir Nicholas Bacon, keeper of the Great Seal, and his wife Lady Ann, sister-in-law of Cecil, Lord Burghley. After a childhood spent in York House he entered Trinity College, Cambridge, in his twelfth year. At his father's death he took to the law hoping for advancement from his uncle, Lord Burghley, who was, however, too much occupied with the rising career of his own son to be helpful to Bacon, who then turned for patronage to Robert Devereux, Earl of Essex. At Essex's downfall and trial, Bacon mercilessly cross-examined him; his subsequent report of the trial, in which he justified his action, has been considered as aggravating his perfidy rather than excusing it. After the accession of James I to the throne Bacon was knighted, was made solicitor-general in 1607, attorney-general in 1613, privy councillor and lord keeper of the Great Seal in 1617 and in the following year he was created Baron Verulam and appointed Lord Chancellor. In his term of office he arraigned for corruption the Earl of Suffolk the then Lord Treasurer, and Sir Henry Yelverton who had succeeded Bacon as attorney-general. At the pinnacle of success he was made Viscount St Alban in January 1621, but downfall followed swiftly. His enemies accused him of corruption and pursued him relentlessly. There is no doubt that he had acted imprudently and, often almost unawares, had accepted money from litigants, but there is no evidence that he ever permitted such gifts to influence the course of justice, so that, though technically guilty of accepting bribes, he may well have been morally innocent. In May 1621, only four months after the first hint of disaster, he was called to the bar of the House, fined £40,000 and committed to the Tower, and though the sentence of imprisonment was remitted, he was banished for ever from the Court.

Bacon's influence on philosophy, particularly on the development of natural philosophy (or experimental science) was considerable. His publications were many, the most notable being the *Advancement of Learning* (1605) and *Novum Organum* (1620). Curiously enough he rejected the Copernican view of the solar system. When compared with the works of his contemporary, Galileo, his writings, despite the largeness of ideas, are inferior; not only are his grandiose schemes unfinished, but he betrays insufficient appreciation of the guiding part to be played by theory in the progress of science, and of the role of mathematics in the growth of physics. However, his views, especially on the need for stringent testing of scientific evidence, had much to do with the subsequent development of science and particularly of the ideals leading to the foundation of the Royal Society and animating its deliberations thenceforward. True to his own precepts he garnered information whenever opportunity offered, and his death resulted from a chill caught one winter's day when, in order to test the preservative powers of cold, he dismounted from his carriage to stuff a chicken with snow gathered from hillside drifts.

BECQUEREL, Antoine Henri (1852–1908), was born in Paris on 15 December and was educated at the École Polytechnique where in 1895 he was made professor. He had entered the department *des ponts et chaussées* where ultimately he became *ingénieur en chef*. In 1896, while investigating the fluorescence of uranium salts he discovered the phenomenon of radioactivity, for which, jointly with Pierre and Marie Curie, he was awarded the Nobel prize for 1903.

BLACKETT, Patrick Maynard Stuart (1897–), was born in London on 18 November and was educated at Osborne and Dartmouth. He served in the Royal Navy during 1914–19, and then having obtained a degree at Cambridge, he joined Rutherford at the Cavendish laboratory in research on cosmic rays, for which he devised an automatic counter-controlled version of C. T. R. Wilson's cloud-chamber. In 1933, simultaneously with C. D. Anderson in America, he and G. P. T. Occhialini announced the discovery of the positron. In that year Blackett was elected to a fellowship in the Royal Society and was made professor at Birkbeck College, London; four years later he succeeded Lawrence Bragg at Manchester. While there he had much to do with the development of radio-astronomy and with the erection of the steerable radio-telescope at Jodrell Bank. In 1948 he was awarded the Nobel prize for his work on cosmic radiation. He succeeded G. P. Thomson at the Imperial College of Science and Technology in 1953, where he remained until in 1963 he retired and devoted himself more fully to politics. He joined the Labour Government as scientific adviser to the Ministry of Technology, though on becoming President of the Royal Society in 1965 he relinquished the appointment except as a part time occupation. In appearance he still has something of the naval officer about him, and his colleagues are apt to be devoted to him.

BOHR, Niels Henrik David (1885–1962), was born in Copenhagen on 7 October and after taking his degree went to work with J. J. Thomson in Cambridge in 1911 and with Rutherford in Manchester the next year. As a result of these contacts he was led to explain the spectra of atomic hydrogen and helium in terms of Rutherford's nuclear model of the atom. Rutherford was critical of the first draft of his paper and persuaded Bohr to amplify and explain his argument in detail. Bohr proposed to quantize the angular momentum of the rotating electron and this together with his postulate of stationary or non-radiating states of the atom provided the basis of the quantum theory of spectra later elaborated by Arnold Sommerfeld into an elegant and comprehensive structure. Sommerfeld was able to achieve so much only because of another principle enunciated by Bohr, the correspondence principle, which states that if the quantum numbers become large the results predicted by the quantum and classical theories converge to equality. As quantum theory could predict only the frequencies, and classical theory the intensities, the correspondence principle was indispensable in the days before Heisenberg or Schrödinger had invented matrix and wave mechanics. Bohr, who had become lecturer at Copenhagen in 1914, went to Manchester in 1915 but returned next year to take up a professorship in Copenhagen where he was made director of the Institute for Theoretical Physics in 1920. In 1922 he received the Nobel prize. In 1939 he visited Princeton, N.J., where, with J. A. Wheeler, he put forward the 'liquid droplet' theory of nuclear fission. He had to flee from Denmark in 1943 to escape Nazi domination and he worked in the U.S.A., chiefly at Los Alamos. Returning to Copenhagen in 1945 he, with Lise Meitner and Otto R. Frisch, elaborated the droplet theory of the nucleus. He propounded the principle of complementarity to resolve the antinomy between wave and particle-like properties of photons and electrons, a philosophical doctrine which he extended to all fields of knowledge.

BOLTZMANN, Ludwig (1844–1906), was born on 20 February in Vienna, where he was educated and where he spent a great part of his life. Having graduated from the University in 1869 he went to teach at Gratz but returned to Vienna in 1873, staying there four years before going back to Gratz. In 1890 he migrated to Munich but after five years returned once more to Vienna where, except for two years at Leipzig from 1900 to 1902, he remained until his death. He worked in the fields of thermodynamics, kinetic theory and radiation. Independently of Stefan he discovered the law relating the total radiation from any body with the fourth power of its absolute temperature; the law is therefore known as the Stefan-Boltzmann law; for similar reasons the statistics used to describe the behaviour of an assemblage of gas molecules at moderate temperatures is called Maxwell-Boltzmann statistics. The universal constant k defining the average energy of the molecules is named Boltzmann's constant although, in his autobiography, Max Planck disputed the propriety of this, maintaining that Boltzmann himself had no conception of its true significance.

BORN, Max (1882–), was born in Breslau on 11 December and was educated in Breslau, Heidelberg, Zürich, Göttingen and Cambridge. A *privatdozent* at Göttingen, he became professor in Berlin in 1915, in Frankfurt-am-Main in 1919, and in Göttingen in 1921.

He was a refugee from Hitler in 1933 and taught in Cambridge for three years before he was appointed Tait Professor of Natural Philosophy in Edinburgh, where he remained until his retirement in 1953. In 1939 he became a British subject, and was elected to a fellowship of the Royal Society. Perhaps his greatest contribution to quantum theory was his appointment of Werner Heisenberg as his research assistant, with whom he and Jordan pioneered so much that was fundamental in quantum mechanics. His well-known work in crystal lattice theory is one of his major achievements. He is the author of a number of books, one of which, *Optik*, now revised and rewritten in English with Emil Wolf and other contributors, was originally in the form of lectures dictated by him to two students each morning at breakfast, so he told the writer. His kindly consideration, his friendly sincerity, his manifest intellectual stature, inspire tremendous liking and respect in all who meet him.

BOWDOIN, James (1727–90), was born in Boston, Massachusetts, on 8 August. He graduated from Harvard College in 1745 and two years later on the death of his father, a wealthy merchant, he inherited a considerable fortune which allowed him to indulge his taste for scientific speculation. He visited Benjamin Franklin in 1751 and thereafter maintained a lifelong correspondence with him, some of his letters concerned with electrical phenomena being of sufficient interest for Franklin to read them before the Royal Society of London. From 1779 Bowdoin was a fellow of Harvard until 1785 when he became colonial Governor of Massachusetts. He was honoured by the universities of Yale and Edinburgh, he was founder and first president of the American Academy of Arts and Sciences and his scientific writings are to be found in the first volume of its Memoirs.

de BRAHE, Tycho (1546–1601), a Danish nobleman of Swedish origin was born on 14 December at Knudstrup near Lund. While in his cot he was kidnapped by his uncle, an admiral and country squire, who brought him up and sent him at thirteen years of age to study Latin at the University of Copenhagen. While he was there an eclipse of the sun deflected his interests and science gained one of its most colourful figures. Wealthy, boastful, generous and quarrelsome, this swashbuckling bravo had his nose sliced off by a fellow student whom he had challenged to a duel in order to chastise his presumption in claiming to be the better mathematician of the two. Tycho constructed for himself a false nose variously reputed to be of gold, silver or wax (possibly of all three); it soothed his hurt pride, but it had the disconcerting habit of falling off with a clatter at the climax of some heated argument. The vigour of his enthusiasms infected King Frederick II, whom he persuaded to give him a site on the island of Hven and to bear the cost of building and equipping a palatial observatory which he called Uraniborg. There he was visited by the famous of the period, including James I, who must have had his royal vanity flattered when, in response to his inquiry how he might recompense his host for his generous intellectual and gastronomic fare, Tycho Brahe answered, 'By the gift of some of your own verses, Sire.' This swaggering nobleman must have scandalized the Court in 1573 when he married a peasant girl, but Frederick continued to shower him with favours. However at Frederick's death in 1588 the courtly climate changed, so that in 1598 Brahe went to Benetek near Prague, where he set about persuading the Emperor Rudolf II to build him a second Uraniborg. He brought Kepler there, but the partnership was broken less than two years later by his sudden death of a burst bladder – incurred because, with exaggerated courtesy, he would not disturb his guests by leaving the dining table to pass water.

Tycho Brahe had a ruling passion, in surprising contrast to his many flamboyancies, a passion for exact observation. The telescope had not yet been invented, so all astronomical observations had to be made with open sights. But such was the precision of Tycho Brahe's measurements that Kepler (by spending six years covering nine thousand folio sheets with close figuring) was able to demonstrate the Ptolemaic theory of planetary motions to be in undoubted conflict with observation. Although the discrepancy was but eight minutes of arc – no more than a quarter of the apparent diameter of the moon – it was enough to force Kepler to abandon the old system and to embrace the Copernican theory. The vast intellectual structures of physics and astronomy are founded on those eight minute subdivisions of a single degree.

BREWSTER, David (1781–1868), was born on 11 December at Jedburgh; he entered the university of Edinburgh at the age of twelve and was educated for the ministry, receiving his licence to preach from the Edinburgh presbytery. He gave up his ministry for science, to which his chief contributions were concerned with the polarization of light. He was knighted in 1832 and in 1837 became principal of the United College of St Leonard and St Salvator in St Andrews, Fife. He only relinquished this position after twenty-three years, to become Vice-Chancellor of Edinburgh University.

His numerous writings include his well-known biography of Newton and shorter accounts of the lives of Galileo, Tycho Brahé and Kepler.

de BROGLIE, Louis Victor Pierre Raymond (1892–), 7th Duc, was born at Dieppe on 15 August, and went to school at the Lycée Jansen de Sailly in Paris. Before the First World War he studied the arts and then physics and from 1914–19 he served in the Radio Télégraphie Militaire. He returned to Paris to study physics at the University, where, in 1932 he became professor. His famous hypothesis of the wave-nature of the electron was put forward in the thesis that he submitted for his doctorate in 1924, and for this fundamental speculation he was awarded the Nobel prize for 1929. He has written books on quantum mechanics and on the philosophical implications of the wave and particle duality.

CHADWICK, James (1891–). Born in Manchester on 20 October, he was educated in Manchester, Cambridge, and at the Charlottenburg Institution in Berlin under H. Geiger. In 1922 he became director of research at the Cavendish Laboratory, Cambridge, concerned also with undergraduate teaching laboratories. He became a fellow of the Royal Society in 1927, and discovered the neutron in 1932. For his discovery of this fundamental constituent of the atomic nucleus he was awarded the Nobel prize in 1935, and in the same year he became professor at Liverpool. He was knighted in 1945. On his retirement in 1948 he became Master of Gonville and Caius College, Cambridge until 1958. He now lives in Wales.

COMPTON, Arthur Holly (1892–1962), was born at Wooster, Ohio, on 10 September, and was educated at Wooster College and Princeton, N.J. He became professor at Washington University, St Louis, Missouri, whence he migrated to Chicago in 1923. In 1927 he gained the Nobel prize for his discovery of the change of wavelength when X-rays are scattered, a prize which he shared with C. T. R. Wilson, whose invention of the cloud-chamber made possible so many discoveries in nuclear physics. In 1945 Compton became Chancellor of his former University at St Louis.

COPERNICUS, Nicholaus (1473–1543), who was born on 14 February, was educated at the University of Cracow from 1491 until he went to Bologna in 1497. Having been elected to a canonry at Frauenberg he took his seat there in 1501, but left again to study at Padua for four years, afterwards returning to live permanently at Frauenberg, where he exercised his medical skill chiefly for the benefit of the poor. He grew intensely interested in astronomy, but finding distasteful the complicated arrangement of epicycles necessary to the Ptolemaic system, he set to work to read deeply in Greek philosophy. He found that the heliocentric hypothesis had been suggested as early as the third century B.C., but it was not until he had worked out its consequences that he became deeply enamoured of its simplicity and elegance, and, though soon convinced of its truth, he made no move to publish his beliefs. His pupil and friend Georg Joachim Rhäticus persuaded him to expound his views in writing, and *De revolutionibus orbium coelestium* was the result. Pope Clement VII approved of the work, and gave a formal request that it should be published. Copernicus was failing in health, and Andreas Osiander, to whom the work of publication was entrusted, took on himself to write a preface explaining that the theory expounded laid no claim to reality, but was merely a convenient and elegant manner of description to facilitate calculations. Apparently he did so to avert the wrathful criticism that he feared from the churchmen, and there is no evidence that Copernicus himself had any doubts of the truth of his theory. The great work was published in 1543 and tradition has it that a copy was put into his hands on his deathbed.

CROOKES, William (1832–1919). Born in London on 17 June, he studied at the Royal College of Chemistry under A. W. von Hoffmann, whose assistant he became in 1851. In 1854 he spent a year as assistant at the Radcliffe Observatory in Oxford and next year took up chemical work at Chester. He discovered the element thallium in 1861 and while investigating this he noticed the radiometer effect now associated with his name, which in turn led to his work on the discharge of electricity in gases and his discovery of what he called radiant matter, later proved by J. J. Thomson to consist of streams of electrons. He was concerned with the health of labourers exposed to radiation from furnaces, and the heat-resistant and ultra-violet opaque glasses he invented are named after him. He was an ardent proponent of increasing the fertility of the land by the use of artificial fertilizers, foreseeing that the yields then usual would not continue to support a rapidly expanding population. He was knighted in 1897 and received the Order of Merit in 1910.

DAVISSON, Clinton Joseph (1881–1959), was born in Bloomington, Illinois on 27 October, was educated at the University of Chicago, Illinois, and at Princeton, N.J., and in 1911 became instructor in physics at the Carnegie Institute of Technology at Pittsburg, Penn. In 1917 he went to work in the Bell Telephone Laboratories, where, in 1927, he demonstrated the diffraction of electrons from a nickel crystal; for this he was awarded the Nobel prize in 1932 jointly with G. P. Thomson. In 1947 he retired from industry and was for two years professor of physics at the University of Virginia.

DEBYE, Peter (1884–), born at Maastricht, Holland, on 14 March; he was educated at Maastricht and then at the Technische Hochschule at Aachen, where he took a degree in electrical engineering and then went to Munich, becoming a *privatdozent* there in 1910 and professor of theoretical physics in Zurich in 1911, and migrating to Utrecht for a year before going to Gottingen for seven years. From there he went to the Eidgenössische Technische Hochschule in Switzerland in 1920 until in 1927 he went to Leipzig. In 1934 he became director of the Max Planck Institut in Berlin, and in 1936 he received the Nobel award for his contributions to chemistry. In 1939 he fled to the U.S.A., becoming professor at Cornell University, Ithaca, N.Y., where he retired in 1952.

DIRAC, Paul Adrien Maurice (1902–), the son of a Swiss father and an English mother, was born in Bristol on 8 August, took a degree in engineering and mathematics at the University of Bristol and went to Cambridge in 1923 where he was elected a fellow of St John's College in 1930 and Lucasian professor of mathematics in 1932. He had been made a fellow of the Royal Society in 1930 and three years later he shared the Nobel prize for Physics with Erwin Schrödinger. Heisenberg's creation of matrix mechanics and Schrödinger's development of wave mechanics fired Dirac's interest in quantum theory to which he himself soon made outstanding contributions. In the *Quantum theory of the electron* published in 1928 he replaced the second order Schrödinger equation by four simultaneous first order equations, which when solved produced almost miraculously the then known properties of the electron, including its spin and magnetic moment. However there were in addition an infinity of solutions of negative energy which, being inexplicable, were thought by his critics to be a blemish on his theory. However in 1930 Dirac interpreted these to indicate a background, or 'sea' of states from which a missing electron would appear as a positive 'hole'; in 1932 the discovery of the positron by Anderson and by Blackett and Occhialini vindicated his prediction.

EINSTEIN, Albert (1879–1955), the greatest mathematical physicist of the age, was born on 14 March at Ulm in Germany; he went to school at Munich and later at Aarau in Switzerland, whence he went to the Polytechnic at Zürich in 1896. He became a Swiss citizen in 1900 and took employment in the Patent Office at Berne; in 1905 he published the four great papers of his life's work: on the special theory of relativity, on the equivalence of mass and energy, on Brownian motion and on the photon theory of light. For this last he was awarded the Nobel prize in 1922. He became a professor at Zürich in 1909, at Prague in 1910 and at the Swiss Federal Polytechnic in 1912. In 1913 he went to Berlin to become professor at the University and director of the Kaiser Wilhelm Institut and in 1916 he announced his general theory of relativity. He went to California in 1932, to Princeton, N.J., in 1933 and became a citizen of the U.S.A. in 1940. He was strongly opposed to the probabilistic trend of modern physics, saying he did not believe that God played dice with the world. He aimed at a unified theory of electromagnetic and gravitational fields, and believed that all physics should ultimately reduce to geometry. His character was outstanding, of a noble simplicity and integrity, gentle, benevolent and humorous, and he had a passionate and lifelong devotion to the cause of social justice. He was an ardent Zionist.

FARADAY, Michael (1791–1867), was born on 22 September to an extremely impoverished family. At fourteen he was apprenticed to a book-binder, and when he was twenty-one a client, a Mr Dance, took him to lectures by Sir Humphrey Davy at the Royal Institution. Faraday subsequently wrote up his lecture notes which so impressed Dance that he persuaded him to let him send them to Davy. The next year Davy, needing an assistant, offered the work to Faraday. After travelling Europe with Davy, he returned to spend the rest of his life at the Royal Institution. Faraday's researches there covered almost every branch of physical and chemical science and technology. In 1821 he constructed a primitive electric motor, something Wollaston had tried and failed to do. In 1824 Faraday was elected to the Royal Society and in 1825 he became director of the Royal Institution. He discovered benzene and butylene, he liquefied chlorine and other gases, he made various highly refracting glasses and the first of the stainless steels. His most important discoveries were crowded into a few days in the summer of 1831.

On 29 August he discovered the laws of electromagnetic induction, phenomena to which we owe our modern electrical power industry. He subsequently applied his discoveries to construct a primitive electric dynamo but his equally important invention of the electric motor was forgotten for fifty years and only rediscovered by accident at an exhibition in Vienna when a mechanic connected together two dynamos, one of which was being driven by a steam engine, with the result that the second resting machine was set into motion, as Faraday, had he then been alive to consult, could have told him would happen. Faraday explained magnetic and electric phenomena by means of his concept of lines of force constituting a field surrounding magnets, electric currents and electric charges. This concept pervades modern physical theory and Einstein called it the greatest creation of the scientific mind. In 1833 Faraday discovered the laws of electrolysis and in 1837 elucidated the phenomena of dielectric materials. In 1841 he fell ill of a mental disorder reminiscent of Newton's, and it was after his recovery from this malady that in 1845 he made the fundamentally significant discovery of the intimate connexion between electromagnetism and light, by demonstrating the magneto-optical effect now known by his name. Faraday was modest and sincere, unassuming yet with a touch of pride: he refused honours from his sovereign, and would accept neither a knighthood nor a peerage, nor would he take upon himself the presidency of the Royal Society as he was urged to do in 1857. He was fiercely devoted to science and at the same time was a convinced and practising member of a small fundamentalist and excessively puritanical sect to which his parents had belonged and which he joined shortly after his marriage.

du FAY, Charles François de Cisternay (1698–1739), the French chemist who was the first to recognize that there are two kinds of electrification, which he named vitreous and resinous but which were later renamed positive and negative by Franklin. du Fay's researches included investigation of the phenomena of phosphorescence and double refraction, and the behaviour of the magnetic needle.

FERMI, Enrico (1901–54), born at Rome on 29 September, he was admitted to the Reale Scuola Normale of the University of Pisa and in 1922 went to Göttingen to work with Max Born and to Leyden to work with Ehrenfest. In 1924 he was appointed a lecturer in Florence and three years later he became professor in Rome, in the same year that he published his account of the statistical treatment of elementary particles. He explained β-decay of radioactive nuclei in 1934 and in 1938 he was awarded the Nobel prize for his work on radioactivity induced by absorption of slow neutrons. He went to Sweden to receive the award, but because of Mussolini's actions he did not return to Italy but went to U.S.A., becoming professor at Columbia University, N.Y., and later at Chicago University. He worked on the atomic energy project, and on 2 December 1942 a self-sustaining chain reaction was started in the first atomic pile, built under his direction at Chicago. Because of this and because it was his work that led to the discovery of nuclear fission by Hahn, Meitner and Frisch, he has been called the father of the atomic bomb. He became a U.S. citizen in 1945.

FITZGERALD, George Francis (1851–1901), born on 3 August at Dublin, was an undergraduate at Trinity College, Dublin, where he was elected to a fellowship in 1877 and to the professorship of natural and experimental philosophy in 1881. He became a fellow of the Royal Society in 1883. He was remarkable for his wide knowledge of physics and for his brilliant speculations. His name is remembered for his celebrated explanation of the failure of the Michelson-Morley experiment to determine the absolute velocity of the observer through space, but it is not so well known that his study of the discharge of an electrical condenser led him to suggest that this discharge might generate electro-magnetic waves, as Hertz shortly discovered was indeed true.

FRANKLIN, Benjamin (1706–90), born in Boston, had a good schooling until he was ten years old, after which he was set to help his father in his business of tallow chandler and soap-boiler. He was so restless in this work that after two years he was apprenticed to his half-brother James, a printer. He moved to Philadelphia in 1723, where the governor of Pennsylvania inspired him to voyage to London in 1724. After some adventures and mishaps he returned to Philadelphia in 1726, where he flourished and in 1737 became postmaster. His activities as a citizen, a public figure and a writer, and his love of philosophical discussions, led to the foundation in 1744 of the American Philosophical Society. In 1748 his finances were in such good shape that he was able to retire from business and devote himself to science and later to politics. He became a fellow of the Royal Society in 1750 and in 1751 he published in England his investigations of the Leyden jar as a means of storing electricity and propounded his one-fluid theory. In 1752 he carried out his famous experiment with the kite. He went to England on political business in 1757 and again in 1764, remaining until 1775. He assisted in drawing up the Declaration of Independence in 1776 and then sailed to France as ambassador to the court of Louis XVI. It is impossible to detail all his discoveries, inventions and activities within the compass of a short paragraph, or to indicate adequately the many facets of his character. Arthur Koestler says that the towering genius of Benjamin Franklin sticks out of the eighteenth century like his own lightning rod, and one of his biographers, in an access of adulation, called him the first civilized American. This man of culture, scientist, statesman and diplomat, a writer of masterly lucidity and style, was converted at the age of sixteen to a belief in the transmigration of souls, and to avoid the risk of eating some reincarnated fellow human, became a lifelong vegetarian.

FRISCH, Otto Robert (1904–), born in Vienna on 1 October, he became Jacksonian professor at Cambridge in 1947, having worked at the Kaiser–Wilhelm Institut in Berlin, where he was concerned, with his aunt, Lise Meitner, and Otto Hahn in discovering the fission of the atomic nuclei of uranium subjected to neutron bombardment.

GALILEI, Galileo (1564–1642), was one of the intellectual giants of science. The son of a musician, he was born at Pisa on 15 February and was educated at the monastery of Vallombrosa near Florence. In 1581 he became a medical student in the University of Pisa, where he is reputed to have made his celebrated observation of the sanctuary lamp swinging pendulum fashion from the roof of the cathedral. He gave up the study of medicine for mathematics, but for lack of money he left the University in 1585 to lecture at the Florentine Academy, where in the next year he published an account of his hydrostatic balance. This brought him fame throughout Italy and two years later an essay on the centre of gravity of solid bodies won him a lectureship in Mathematics at Pisa. He moved to Padua in 1592 where he stayed for eighteen years and whence he published his laws of motion of falling bodies in 1604. He had written to Kepler in 1597 but did not continue the correspondence fearing ridicule because of his leanings towards Copernican doctrines. Having heard in Venice of the newly invented telescope he immediately constructed one for himself and the next year, in 1610, he announced many astronomical discoveries, especially the resolution of the Milky Way into innumerable stars, his observation of the satellites of Jupiter, of spots on the sun, of the phases of Venus, and of the peculiar protuberances on Saturn which periodically altered in appearance. Shortly thereafter he was appointed philosopher and mathematician to the Grand Duke of Tuscany. In 1611 he demonstrated his telescope in Rome,

86

and two years later he published his thoughts on sun spots. However in 1616 Copernicus's book was condemned and put on the Index Prohibitorum, and Galileo thought it expedient to go into retirement at Bellosguardo for the next seven years. In 1623 he dedicated his polemic *Saggiatore* (written in reply to a pamphlet directed against him) to Pope Urban VI, who received it enthusiastically, and the next year Galileo went to Rome hoping to obtain revocation of the 1616 decree, but without success. In 1632 he published his masterpiece, *Dialogue on the Two Chief World Systems*, but in Rome the next year he had to stand trial for his views, and for eight years thereafter he suffered house arrest at Arcetri. In 1634 he wrote the *Dialogue of Two New Sciences* (not printed until 1638). He discovered the libration of the moon in 1736 shortly before becoming blind, but even when blind, among other things he designed a pendulum regulator for a clock (later constructed by Christian Huygens in 1656). During his long life his contributions to science and especially to astronomy were immense, but his most enduring influence was his belief in the marriage of physics and mathematics that has been the inspiration of physicists through succeeding centuries.

GALVANI, Luigi or Aloisio (1737–98), was born on 9 September in Bologna where he spent his life studying and teaching medicine and anatomy. One windy day, having hung some dissected frogs' legs by copper hooks from an iron rail, he noticed a violent muscular contraction whenever the wind blew them into contact with the rail. He mistakenly believed the phenomenon to be due to animal electricity conducted through the metallic junction, and it was only much later that Volta correctly explained the galvanic effect as originating in the chemical action of the saline solution upon the two dissimilar metals, and was able to use it to generate a continuous current of electricity. The oft-repeated story that Galvani discovered the effect in 1786 when dissecting a frog with a steel scalpel near the sparks from an electrostatic machine is an anachronism, for he had written of the muscular stimulation by a metallic pair some twenty years earlier. This distinguished and devoted physiologist was dismissed from his professorship in 1797 because he refused on religious grounds to take the oath of allegiance to the newly formed Cisalpine Republic, and though a move was made to reinstate him he died before this could be done.

GAMOW, George (1904–), was born on 4 March in Odessa, Russia, studied at the Universities of Leningrad, Copenhagen and

Cambridge; in 1931 he became master of research in Leningrad, and lectured in Paris and London during 1933–34. He then went to the U.S.A., to be professor of theoretical physics at George Washington University, where he remained until in 1956 he became professor at the University of Colorado. He explained the escape of α-particles from a radioactive nucleus as a tunnelling process in consequence of their wave properties. He is the author of many works written to interpret modern physics to the layman.

GILBERT, William (1544–1603), born on 24 May at Colchester, was educated at Colchester Grammar School and at St John's College, Cambridge. After taking his M.D. he travelled in Italy for four years and then settled in medical practice in London. He was appointed physician to the Queen shortly before her death, but he died, probably of the plague, in November 1603. He was a strong advocate of the Copernican view of the solar system, but although his contributions to the science of the time were many and varied, his chief claim to fame rests on his great book *de Magnete*, published in 1600, in which he described his researches in magnetism.

von GOETHE, Johann Wolfgang (1749–1832), was born at Frankfurt-am-Main on 28 August. The son of a well-to-do lawyer who practised but little, he was taught at home, largely by his father. His great fame is as poet and dramatist, but he began his formal education as a law student at Leipzig, where he fell ill and, after recovering, transferred his studies to Strasbourg. During his convalescence he dabbled in medicine, alchemy, astrology and the occult – not black magic but the mystical *magia naturalis* which seeks communion with extra-terrestrial beings of a higher order of intelligence – an art that is reflected in his *Faustus*. Included in his huge output of writings are three scientific publications: *Die Metamorphose der Pflanzen* (1790), *Beiträg zur Optik* (1792) and *Farbenlehre* (1810). His essay in the theory of colour was ill-judged, and one marvels that, having no mathematics, he had the temerity to launch so violent an attack on Newton. But his botanical and physiological observations were acute, and his recognition of organic evolution paved the way for Darwin's theory of the origin of species.

HAHN, Otto (1879–), born on 8 March at Frankfurt-am-Main, he was educated at Marburg and Munich and went to work at University College, London with William Ramsay in 1904, and the next year with Ernest Rutherford in Montreal. With Lise Meitner at Berlin-Dahlem he discovered the radioactivity of thorium in 1917, and the nuclear fission of uranium and thorium in 1938. He received the Nobel prize for chemistry in 1944 and became president of the Max Planck Institut at Göttingen in 1946, where he remained until his retirement in 1960. In 1957, with seventeen other West German physicists, he refused to co-operate in developing nuclear weapons, and he supported Albert Schweitzer in his demand for the abolition of nuclear bomb tests.

HALLEY, Edmund (1656–1742), was born at Haggerston near London on 29 October and was educated at St Paul's School and Queen's College, Oxford. At the age of nineteen he published a method of finding the aphelion and eccentricity of planetary orbits, and a year later on observing some sunspots he established that the sun rotated on its axis. In order to investigate the variations in the magnetic compass he voyaged for two years (1699–1700) in both hemispheres. He became Savilian professor of geometry at Oxford in 1703 and Astronomer Royal at Greenwich in 1721. He was the first to compute cometary orbits and the most famous of all comets, which returns each century, bears his name. He detected the 'long inequality' in the motions of Jupiter and Saturn, later to be resolved by Laplace, and with remarkable insight he suggested that the aurora borealis was magnetic in origin.

HEISENBERG, Werner Carl (1901–), was born at Würzburg on 5 December. His interest in physics resulted, so he said, from reading a textbook in which the illustrator had crudely portrayed atoms as balls linked together by tiny hooks and eyes such as dressmakers use. He took up the study of physics first at Munich under Arnold Sommerfeld, and then at Göttingen, where he became assistant to Max Born in 1924. There he developed his matrix mechanics, and then in 1926 he went to Copenhagen to work with Niels Bohr. He became professor at Leipzig in 1927, the same year in which he announced his uncertainty relation, or principle of indeterminacy. In 1932 he was awarded the Nobel prize and in 1941 he was made director of the Kaiser-Wilhelm Institut at Berlin; he left in 1946 to become director of the Max Planck Institut at Göttingen, and remained there until in 1958 he was made director of the Max Planck Institut at Munich. His contributions to the development of quantum mechanics are pre-eminent, and the indeterminacy principle that he enunciated strikes to the root of philosophy as well as of physics. It crystallized the transformation of the mechanistic determinism of the Newtonian world as seen

89

through the eyes of Laplace, into the probabilistic indeterminism of a seemingly chance-governed world, in which the laws of physics are the laws of probability, its texture set, not by random thermal motions of atoms as envisaged by Maxwell and Boltzmann, but by the nature of energy itself, the ultimate constituent of the universe.

von HELMHOLTZ, Herman Ludwig Ferdinand (1821–94), was born at Potsdam on 31 August. He became professor of physiology in Königsberg in 1849. He went to Bonn in 1855, to Heidelberg in 1858, and then in 1871 became professor of physics at Berlin. In 1887 he was appointed director of the physio-technical institute at Charlottenburg. His work was spread over many fields, for always he was able to perceive connexions between widely differing phenomena. His important books, *Physiological Optics* (1856–66) and *Sensations of Tone* (1862) in which he advocated Young's three-colour theory of vision, and put forward his own theory of the sympathetic vibration of the basilar membrane of the cochlea of the inner ear, are well known, and for many decades remained the standard works on their subjects. He left his impress on much of physics and physiology. With his paper of 1847, *The Conservation of Force*, he laid the foundations of the principle of conservation of energy and his invention in 1851 of the ophthalmoscope did much for clinical practice, as well as for research. He was the first to measure the speed of an impulse along a nerve, and in 1871 he attempted to measure the speed of propagation of electromagnetic induction. He found that this was very great, probably greater than 314,000 metres per second. This brilliant experimentalist was wrapped up in his own researches; Max Planck, who studied under him, records that his lectures were ill-prepared, ill-delivered, and even uninspiring!

HERTZ, Heinrich Rudolf (1857–94), was born in Hamburg on 22 February. He studied engineering, but transferred his interest to physics and worked under Helmholtz in Berlin. In 1883 he went to Kiel as *privatdozent* and two years later became professor at the Karlsruhe Polytechnic, where he discovered the electromagnetic waves predicted by Maxwell. In 1889 he succeeded Clausius at Bonn, and died there after a lengthy illness.

JEANS, James Hopwood (1877–1946), was born in London on 11 September and in 1898 entered Trinity College, Cambridge. He was professor of mathematics at Princeton, New Jersey, U.S.A., from 1905 to 1909 and professor of astronomy at the Royal Institution in London from 1924 to 1929. For twenty-one years he was research associate of Mount Wilson Observatory, California. He received the Order of Merit in 1939. His chief work was in kinetic theory, the theory of radiation and cosmogony. He was the author of many popular scientific books; of one of these – *The Mysterious Universe* – *Punch* remarked that the universe was not nearly so mysterious as Jeans's book about it.

KELVIN, William Thomson, Baron of Largs (1824–1907), was born in Belfast, Ireland, on 26 June, and at the age of eleven entered the University of Glasgow where his father had become professor of mathematics. In 1841 he left there for Peterhouse, Cambridge, where in 1845 he was Smith's prizeman and second wrangler. He studied in Paris for a year under Regnault, and then went back to Glasgow to be professor there for the next fifty-three years. In 1847 he and Joule met and the next year he proposed the absolute thermodynamic scale of temperature; in 1851 he published his great paper on heat which reconciled the work of Sadi Carnot, Rumford, Davy, Mayer and Joule. From 1854 on he was interested in submarine telegraphy and, with George Gabriel Stokes, developed the mathematics of transmission of electrical signals by cable. He then turned his attention to navigational problems and, as well as compiling accurate tide tables and simplifying and improving the art of obtaining a fix on a ship's position at sea, he completely transformed the design of the ship's compass, greatly increasing its accuracy and reliability. He was foremost in establishing electrical standards, and his demonstration of the oscillatory nature of an electrical discharge from a Leyden jar was to lead Hertz to the generation of the electromagnetic waves later exploited by Marconi and others. He was knighted in 1866 and created Baron Kelvin of Largs in 1890; he was made President of the Royal Society in 1902 and Chancellor of the University of Glasgow in 1904. In this same year he published a revised version of the lectures on the wave theory of light that he had delivered at Johns Hopkins University, Baltimore, Maryland, U.S.A., twenty years earlier. At his death in 1907 his body was buried in Westminster Abbey.

KEKULÉ von Stradonitz, Friedrich August (1829–96), was born at Darmstadt on 7 September and studied architecture at Giessen. There Julius von Liebig came to have influence upon him and he changed over to the study of chemistry. He went to Paris in 1851 and next year became personal assistant to Stenhouse in England. In 1853 he went to Heidelberg where he worked in his own laboratory, becoming a *privatdozent* in 1856 but leaving two years later to be professor of chemistry at Ghent. From 1865 until his death he was professor at Bonn; while there he was ennobled and took the title of von Stradonitz. Organic chemistry in all its branches owes much to Kekulé for it was he who, in 1858, brought evidence to bear to show that the carbon atom was quadrivalent, but his chief contribution was the ring structure that he proposed for benzene in 1865.

KEPLER, Johann (1571–1630), was born at Würtemburg on 27 December, the son of the daughter of the burgomaster by her ne'er-do-well husband, a soldier of fortune who, having lost all he had, tried his hand at tavern keeping and because that failed, ultimately deserted his wife and family in 1589. Kepler survived an attack of smallpox when he was only three years old, but the disease left him with crippled hands and poor eyesight. In 1577 – the year in which there was a great comet in the sky – he started school at Leonburg but the family was so poor that he soon left to work in the fields. His physique was too frail for such labour and in 1584 he entered Adeburg seminary to train for the priesthood; two years later he transferred to Maulbronn. In 1588 his performance in the examination for the bachelor's degree was so brilliant that he was accepted at the University of Tübingen, where Michael Maestlin became his teacher and lifelong friend and imbued him with Copernican doctrines. In 1594 he was offered the professorship of astronomy at Gratz which he accepted only with reluctance, for it seemed that his chief duty would be the preparation of astrological almanacs. Although he threw himself into the work with assiduity he found time to pursue his own mystical researches into the architecture of the solar system; in 1595 he published *Mysterium Cosmographicum* in which he announced his theory that the planetary distances are dictated by the geometry of the five regular solids. This brought him to the notice of the great Danish astronomer Tycho Brahe who invited him to Prague; on the sudden and unexpected death of Tycho Brahe in 1601 he succeeded him as Imperial Astronomer to the Emperor Rudolf II. As a court official his responsibilities included the casting of horoscopes for important personages and occasions; in this occupation he excused himself by saying that nature, which gave every animal the means of subsistence, gave astrology to be an adjunct and ally to astronomy.

His optical discoveries were published in 1604 and his discovery of the elliptical shape of the orbit of Mars was made in 1609, in the same year that he explained the cause of the tides. The next year his Imperial patron presented him with a telescope then newly invented by Galileo, and a year later he published *Dioptrice* in which he suggested the principle of the astronomical (or inverting) telescope used ever since. That year was one of deep grief to Kepler for he lost his favourite child from smallpox and shortly afterwards his wife died of typhus. He assuaged his sorrow by devoting himself to his attempts to understand the motions of the heavenly bodies and by 1619 he had discovered the last of his famous three laws which he published in his book *De Harmonice Mundi*; his exposition of Copernican theories appeared in *Epitome Astronomiae Copernicae* from 1618–21. At this date domestic troubles once more overwhelmed him, for his mother, whose unbridled tongue had earned her the hatred of her neighbours, a hatred which she exacerbated by suing them for slander, was arrested as a witch. Kepler hurried to Würtemburg where he exerted himself indefatigably on her behalf and finally obtained her release; shortly afterwards she died of old age.

Kepler's greatest contribution to astronomy and physics – his enunciation of the three laws of planetary motion – is his lasting memorial, but he should be remembered also for being the first to analyse observations taking into proper account their inevitable errors, and for discovering that the planes of the planetary orbits all pass through the centre of the sun; this discovery is fundamental to physics, for without this knowledge Newton would have had nothing on which to build his theory of gravitation.

LAPLACE, Pierre Simon, Marquis de (1749–1827), was born at Beaumont-en-Auge, Normandy, on 28 March. He entered the University of Caen at the age of sixteen and went to Paris in 1767 where he became professor at the École Militaire. In 1773 he solved the problem that was puzzling astronomers, who had found that the orbit of the planet Jupiter was slowly shrinking while that of Saturn was expanding; he concluded that the changes were periodic with a period of 929 years. His famous work in five volumes, *Traité de Mécanique Céleste*, appeared at intervals from 1799–1825 and his studies of probability in 1812 and 1814 in *La théorie analytique des probabilités* and in *Essai philosophique*. For six weeks in 1799 he was Ministre de l'Interieur, until Napoleon dismissed him saying that he had brought into administrative affairs the spirit of infinitesimals, and promoted him to become a member of the Senate! Later at the restoration of the Bourbons he was created a Marquis. His celebrated reply when in answer to Napoleon's query concerning the place of God in his conception of the

Universe, Laplace confessed that he had no need of Him, epitomized the mechanistic determinism which was the logical fruit of his labours in mathematics and astronomy.

LEVERRIER, Urbain Jean Joseph (1811–77), was born at St Lô, Normandy, on 11 March and was educated at the École Polytechnique in Paris. He did so well in his examinations that he had a free choice of the appointments open to graduates from the school; he chose the administration of tobacco. However in 1837 he became a teacher at the École Polytechnique and in 1844 determined to solve the problem of the erratic motions of the planet Uranus. By 1846 he was able to give the celestial co-ordinates of the point in the heavens at which the planet responsible for the vagaries of Uranus shoud be found, and on 23 September of that year the Berlin astronomer Galle saw the new planet almost precisely at the predicted place. John Couch Adams had anticipated Leverrier's calculations by more than a twelvemonth but because Challis, the Cambridge astronomer to whom he had communicated his results, was unwilling to institute an immediate search for the unknown planet, it was Leverrier's prediction that appeared to have priority. In 1854 Leverrier succeeded Arago as director of the Paris observatory, but by 1870 the storm of protests which he had aroused in his efforts to clean out administrative abuses brought about his removal. His successor died two years later and Leverrier was reinstated, but with safeguards adequate to prevent a recurrence of trouble. In astronomy Leverrier aimed at elaborating on Laplace's *Mécanique Céleste*, and he was convinced that residual aberrations in planetary motion indicated the existence of yet another planet beyond Neptune, which he named Vulcan. There is in fact no such planet, but the anomalies were unexplained until 1915 when Einstein published his general theory of relativity and removed the need for it.

LORENTZ, Hendrik Antoon (1853–1928), was born on 18 July at Arnheim in Holland and was educated at Leyden where in 1878 he became professor of mathematical physics, having previously taught at night-school after taking his bachelor's degree in 1871. He started his researches by discussing the refraction and reflexion of light by dielectrics and metals, and later he developed an expression relating the refractive index and the density of any medium. He grew convinced of the need to construct a consistent theory of light and electromagnetism, and his genius contrived a skilful interweaving of atomistic and field theories. In 1892 and 1895 he published two papers on electrical and optical phenomena in moving media. In these, as was natural at the time, he assumed an ether at absolute rest, but in order to avoid contradictions in his theory, he was compelled in the second paper to introduce the idea of local time. Joseph Larmor pointed out the connexion between this device and the contraction Fitzgerald had postulated to explain the Michelson-Morley experiment. In 1903 Lorentz arrived at a comprehensive treatment in which he obtained expressions, today known as the Lorentz transformations, which are identical with those required by Einstein's special theory of relativity. For his achievements he was awarded the Nobel prize in 1902, sharing it with Pieter Zeeman. In 1923 he became director of the physical laboratory of the Teyler Institute at Haarlem. He was then an internationally known figure with a world-wide reputation whose scientific judgement was highly valued. He was a fine character, modest and patient, who was welcome wherever he went, for his mastery of many languages made him able to participate with ease in any discussion.

MACH, Ernst (1838–1916), was born in Turas, Moravia, on 18 February. He graduated from the university of Vienna in 1860 and, four years later, became professor of mathematics at Gratz; he left there in 1867 to be professor of physics at Prague. His important book *Die Mechanik* was published in 1883. In 1895 a chair of philosophy was created for him in Vienna and though three years later he suffered a stroke, he recovered sufficiently to write *Erkenntnis und Irrtum* which was published in 1905. In his philosophy, science was but an economical way of summarizing experience, and he regarded as metaphysical any physical theory dealing with objects not reducible to sensory experiences. This view greatly influenced Einstein, and had much to do with the rise of the philosophical doctrines of logical positivism in Europe and pragmatism in America.

MARCONI, Guglielmo, Marchese (1874–1937), was born at Bologna on April 25 and studied physics at Leghorn. When he was nineteen he read in a magazine an article on the experiments Hertz was making with electromagnetic waves. He conceived the notion that these waves might be used for telegraphy and within a year he succeeded in signalling with them across the breadth of his garden. The next year he set up transmitters on Salisbury Plain and on the shore of the Bristol Channel, and two years later he succeeded in sending signals across the English Channel from France to the cliffs of Dover. Against advice he persisted in his dream of transatlantic communications and on 12 December 1901 a signal sent from Poldhu in Cornwall was heard faintly in St John's, Newfoundland. In 1909 the successful Marconi, and Braun, who had developed the electron tube invented by Ambrose Fleming, shared the Nobel prize for physics.

MAXWELL, James Clerk (1831–79), was born in Edinburgh on 13 November, went to school at the Edinburgh Academy and entered Edinburgh University in 1847. Having taken his degree in 1850 he went to Peterhouse, Cambridge, and after a few terms migrated to Trinity College. In 1854 he was second wrangler and shared the Smith's prize with the first wrangler E. J. Routh. He became professor of Natural Philosophy at Marischal College, Aberdeen, in 1856 but on the reorganization of the College four years later he went to King's College, London, until 1868. He then retired to his country seat in Kirkcudbrightshire but after three years he was called from this seclusion to be the first Cavendish professor of experimental physics at Cambridge, where he supervised the building of the laboratory. Maxwell published his first scientific paper at the age of fifteen when he wrote for the Royal Society of Edinburgh a description of a mechanical method that he had devised for the drawing of Cartesian ovals; two years later in the Transactions of that Society he published an essay on the equilibrium of elastic solids. In 1854 he wrote a paper on Faraday's conception of lines of force, and in 1859 he won the Adams prize for an analysis of the conditions of stability of Saturn's rings. From 1855 on he wrote extensively on perception of colour and on colour-blindness, and on the kinetic theory of gases. But it was in 1867 that his first paper on the electromagnetic field appeared, and in 1871 at the age of forty-two he published his greatest work *Electricity and Magnetism*. This has been called an intellectual jungle but it contained in one comprehensive survey all the known phenomena of electricity, magnetism and optics. His work remains virtually unchanged today, and his macroscopic treatment was generalized and extended by Lorentz to apply also to atomic and molecular phenomena. One of the merits of the theory of relativity is that it leaves Maxwell's equations unchanged since they are invariant to the Lorentz transformations.

MEITNER, Lise (1878–), was born in Vienna on 7 November. She visited Berlin to hear Max Planck lecture and stayed to work at the Kaiser-Wilhelm Institut for Chemistry, where in 1926 she became professor of physics. In 1938 she fled from the Nazis to take refuge in Stockholm, where she was elected to the Swedish Academy of Sciences which, for a woman, is a rare honour. In 1939 she, Otto Hahn and her nephew Otto Robert Frisch together suggested that the presence of barium after uranium had been bombarded with neutrons indicated that the atomic nucleus had undergone fission.

MICHELSON, Albert Abraham (1852–1931), was born at Strelno on the borders of Prussia on 19 December, and with his parents emigrated to Virginia City, Nevada, U.S.A. He was educated at the U.S. Naval Academy whence he graduated in 1873 and where two years later he became an instructor in physics and chemistry. He left the Navy and for two years studied in Berlin, Heidelberg and Paris; he returned to be professor at the Case Institute in Cleveland, Ohio and there devised his interferometer in order to carry out the experiment originally suggested by Arago many years before. In 1887 he and Morley announced that their attempt to measure the absolute velocity of their laboratory through space gave a null result, thus setting physicists a problem that was not adequately solved until 1905 with the publication of Einstein's special theory of relativity. Michelson moved to Clark University, Worcester, Massachusetts in 1887 but five years later he was made the first professor at the Ryerson Laboratory in the new University of Chicago. There he turned his interferometer to spectroscopic and metrological uses; his determination of the metre in terms of the wavelength of light was a remarkable technical achievement; the method he originated for analysis of the fine structure of a spectral line from observations of the visibility of the fringes seen in his interferometer was a piece of virtuosity that has recently borne rich fruit – under the fertilizing influence of electronic computers modern interferogram spectroscopy can do in minutes what took Michelson many months of laborious calculation. For his many brilliant contributions to experimental optics he gained the Nobel prize for 1907, but again he pioneered in dramatic fashion in 1920 by constructing an interferometer 40 ft wide, with which he found the star called Betelgeuse to be no less than 240,000,000 miles in diameter. The principle of this interferometer is fundamentally that used today with radio-telescopes (though in a more sophisticated form due to Hanbury-Brown and Twiss).

NEWTON, Isaac (1642–1727), was born at Woolsthorpe in Lincolnshire on 25 December. His father had died the previous autumn and when he was three years old his mother remarried, leaving him in the care of his grandmother. At Grantham Grammar School he was but an indifferent student until a fight with another boy so roused him that he set to work to become the top scholar of the school. He was fourteen years old when his mother was again widowed and she took him from school to help on the farm. He proved to be absent-minded and too much engrossed in his own thoughts to be useful and at his uncle's instigation he returned to school in 1660 to prepare for Cambridge, where next year he entered Trinity College as a sub-sizar; three years later he gained a scholarship and in 1665 he took his degree. For the next two years the University and Colleges were closed because of the plague and Newton spent eighteen months isolated at Woolsthorpe. Records of his purchases of a glass prism, a chemical furnace and sundry workshop necessities show that his occupations were experimental as well as mathematical. As a boy he had been mechanically minded, making kites, water wheels, mechanical toys and even a kind of self-propelled carriage; in his maturity he was a superb craftsman, as we know from the reflecting telescope he constructed for which he ground and polished the mirror with his own hands. He later gave the instrument to the Royal Society, which received it with a delight that he found very gratifying. He returned to Cambridge in 1668 to take up the fellowship to which Trinity College had elected him.

Newton was a man of variable moods, at times absorbed and detached, at others almost gay. While still at school he contracted a nominal engagement to marry a Miss Storey, but as life at the University more and more claimed his attention this seems to have faded into oblivion, though he did maintain a lifelong friendship with her. Even while an undergraduate he appears to have had some conception of a universal force which should account for all motion and as the years passed this idea came to dominate his thoughts. His invention of the differential calculus – his method of fluxions – was but an incident in the development of this great theme, which he was in the end persuaded to give to the world with the publication in 1687 of the *Principia*. This monumental work was written in the space of little more than eighteen months and shortly after he had completed it he found himself representing his University as a member of Parliament, where in 1689 he took his seat. Hardly had he done so when his mother fell ill of a fever and he hurriedly left London to nurse her devotedly until her death. The strain of these years told on him so severely that in 1693 he suffered a nervous and mental breakdown. He slowly recovered and took up life again in London, where in 1696 he became War-den, and three years later Master, of the Royal Mint. This brought him comparative affluence which he seems to have enjoyed. He set up house in Jermyn Street with his witty and beautiful young niece Catherine Barton to preside over his household, but though in 1703 he became President of the Royal Society and published his *Opticks* in 1704, he grew increasingly occupied with theological speculations and biblical chronology. He was knighted in 1705 and when his niece married his deputy at the Mint, he and they moved to a fine house in St Martin's Street where he lived until, shortly before his death, he removed to the country air of the village of Kensington. At the age of eighty-four he died and was buried be-side the kings and princes in Westminster Abbey.

OERSTED, Hans Christian (1777–1851), was born on 14 August at Rudköbing in Denmark and studied pharmacy at the University of Copenhagen to which, after travelling extensively, he returned in 1806 to be professor. Among other things he was the first to pre-pare metallic aluminium in 1825, and in 1829 he founded and be-came the first president of the Danish College of Engineering. He was interested in acoustics, but especially in Galvani's discovery of the stimulation of frog's muscle by contact with pairs of dissimilar metals. Convinced of the underlying unity of natural forces, he was for ever attempting to discover an electrical origin of magnetic and chemical phenomena, and it was while actually giving a lec-ture on the evening of 20 April 1820 that he made his historic discovery of the magnetic action of a wire carrying an electric cur-rent. This dramatic event provoked tremendous excitement in the audience, equalled only by the enthusiasm generated in every laboratory in Europe and America. Ampère heard of it in France on 11 September and within a week he had exhaustively investi-gated its consequences; Wollaston heard of it in London and tried to construct a primitive electric motor – an attempt in which he failed but in which Faraday soon succeeded. Oersted was an in-spiring lecturer and teacher, who also wrote many popular articles. The American Physical Society's Oersted Medal, awarded yearly for excellence in the field of physics education, honours both the recipient and the outstanding reputation of the great teacher him-self, though few can hope to rival Oersted by making during the course of their lectures a discovery so significant as his.

PAULI, Wolfgang (1900–58), an Austrian-Swiss, was born in Vienna on 25 April and was educated in Munich under Sommer-feld, in Göttingen under Born and in Copenhagen under Bohr. For five years he was a lecturer in Hamburg and then for thirty years, except for the period of the Second World War which he spent in the U.S.A., he served the Swiss Federal Institute of Technology as professor of theoretical physics. He made numerous contributions to quantum theory, one of the more important being his postulate of nuclear spin put forward to explain the hyperfine structure of spectral lines, but the most important of all is his exclusion principle for which he was awarded the Nobel prize in 1945. This fundamental principle restricts the possible states of electrons in the atom, with the almost miraculous result that the chemical elements fall naturally into the order of the periodic table that Mendeléyev discovered empirically in the middle of the last century.

PLANCK, Max Karl Ernst Ludwig (1858–1947), who propounded the quantum theory, was born at Kiel, Germany, on 22 April. He studied in Berlin under Kirchhoff and Helmholtz and graduated from Munich in 1879. There he taught for five years, becoming professor of mathematics in Kiel and in 1889 succeeding Kirchhoff in Berlin, where he remained until his retirement in 1928. Thinking it his duty to oppose Hitler he stayed in Germany and suffered at the hands of the Nazis until he was rescued by the Americans at the end of the Second World War; his second son was executed by the Germans for his part in the unsuccessful rising against the Führer. Max Planck's work in thermodynamics was based on the teachings of Clausius; it was in March 1900 that he obtained empirically the formula correctly describing the spectral distribution of energy that had been found experimentally by Lummer and Pringsheim; in December of the same year he announced the three postulates of the quantum theory from which, by statistical methods, he derived the formula as a theoretical consequence; this famous formula is everywhere known by his name. Although this inspired piece of pioneering, for which he was awarded the Nobel prize in 1918, was entirely his own, he did not take the lead in subsequent development of the quantum theory, which he always believed was but a temporary stepping stone to more complete understanding.

POINCARÉ, Jules Henri (1854–1912), was born at Nancy in France on 29 April and educated in Paris at the École Polytechnique and the École des Mines. He became a teacher of mathematics at the University of Caen in 1879, and two years later was appointed as professor at Paris. His mathematical researches led him to the understanding of Fuchsian functions and then to the invention of new methods of astronomical calculations which he published in the three volumes of *Les Méthodes nouvelles de la Mécanique Céleste* in 1892, 1893 and 1899. His greatest work, published in 1906, is on the dynamics of the electron; in this he obtained, independently of Einstein, many of the results of the special theory of relativity, deriving them however from detailed analysis of electromagnetism and not, as Einstein derived them, from basic considerations of time and simultaniety.

PROUT, William (1785–1850), was born at Horton in Gloucestershire on 15 January. He became a physician and practised in London; he made various discoveries in biochemistry, the most notable being that the gastric juices contained hydrochloric acid. He is remembered for his suggestion, which he published anonymously, in 1815, that all chemical elements were composed of hydrogen. This idea was discredited for more than a century but was triumphantly vindicated when, in 1932, it became clear that all atomic nuclei are compounded of protons and neutrons; the proton is the bare nucleus of a hydrogen atom and the neutron is a fundamental particle which, when free, can decay into a proton, emitting an electron and a neutrino in the process.

PYTHAGORAS (*circa* 580–495 B.C.), was probably born at Samos in the Aegean Sea. He settled in Croton about 530 B.C. and gathered round him a group of some three hundred persons of both sexes – an ascetic community – who lived their lives by his rules. The invariable retort to any query or proposed infraction of these rules was '*ipse dixit*' which quelled all argument. The members of this almost religious community were pledged to self-control, temperance and vegetarianism and spent their lives in the practice of the arts and crafts, music and gymnastics, and in the study of mathematics and medicine. The community so annoyed the lay inhabitants of Croton by interfering in politics that Pythagoras felt obliged to remove it to Metapontum in about 496 B.C.

It is probable that Pythagoras himself discovered the geometrical theorem, now known to every schoolboy, concerning the squares on the sides of a right-angled triangle, for Plutarch tells us that when he had found it he was so overjoyed that he sacrificed an ox. The Pythagoreans were aware that the earth was a sphere and as early as 500 B.C. had some idea of its diameter. But the knowledge that had the greatest influence was the discovery of the simple numerical relationships between the lengths of vibrating strings that give rise to a musical scale. Pythagoras himself was led to formulate this quantitative law of physics when he observed that the pitch of the sound made by the blacksmith's hammer depended on the length of the iron bar on the anvil. The discovery was undoubtedly the origin of the Pythagorean belief in number as the key to the universe, a mystical concept which dominated natural philosophy until the time of Kepler, and which seems curiously revivified in modern physical theory.

RAYLEIGH, John William Strutt, 3rd Baron (1842–1919), was born on 12 November at Maldon, Essex. He entered Trinity College, Cambridge, and was senior wrangler and Smith's prizeman in 1865. He succeeded Maxwell as Cavendish professor in 1879, but four years later he resigned to become professor of Natural Philosophy at the Royal Institution, where he remained until 1905. He was one of the original recipients of the Order of Merit at its inception in 1902; he became President of the Royal Society in 1905 and Chancellor of Cambridge University in 1908. His breadth of knowledge was extraordinary and his work ranged over the whole field of physics; there is scarcely a topic then known to physicists which he did not touch and that he did not illuminate, as a search through the four volumes of his published papers will quickly reveal, but his outstanding contributions were in acoustics and optics. He was a meticulous experimentalist; it was as the result of a prolonged hunt for the cause of a minute discrepancy that he had found between the atomic weights of nitrogen obtained from the atmosphere and from chemical decomposition that he discovered the rare gas argon; for this he was awarded the Nobel prize in 1904.

RUTHERFORD, Ernest, Baron of Nelson (1871–1937), the son of a farmer, was born in Nelson, N.Z., on 30 August. He entered Nelson College in 1889 and then went to New Zealand University at Wellington whence he graduated with a double first in mathematics and physics in 1893. He gained an 1851 Exhibition to Cambridge to work with J. J. Thomson, first on magnetic detection of radio waves, and then on ionization produced by X-rays and photoelectrons. In 1898 he became professor at McGill University, Montreal, Canada where in the next year he identified α-rays and β-rays from radioactive sources. He returned to England to be professor at Manchester in 1907 and the next year was awarded the Nobel prize for the chemistry of the radioactive series. In 1911 he demonstrated the small size and massive nature of the atomic nucleus; among the students who flocked to him, their imagination fired by this discovery, were Niels Bohr in 1912 and H. G. Moseley in 1913.

After the First World War Rutherford resumed his work on radio-activity and in 1919 he made the first observation of a disintegration of a nitrogen nucleus; in that year he succeeded his former teacher J. J. Thomson as Cavendish professor. He had been knighted in 1914, he became President of the Royal Society and received the Order of Merit in 1925 and was created Baron Rutherford of Nelson in 1931. He had an infectious enthusiasm and a flair for experiment that inspired his research workers to immense efforts. He did not confine his interest to research, but at frequent intervals he would tour the undergraduate laboratories asking pertinent and stimulating questions which required no little knowledge and understanding in his hearers. He died unexpectedly after a surgical operation.

SCHRODINGER, Erwin (1887–1961), was born in Vienna on 12 August and was educated at the University of Vienna and became a professor there in 1921 and then at Stuttgart, Breslau and Zurich in turn. Stimulated by de Broglie's hypothesis of the wave-nature of the electron he developed a wave-mechanical treatment of its motion in the atom, publishing his famous wave equation in 1926. The solutions of this equation represent the stationary states of the atom; as these could be superimposed their beat frequency appeared as emitted radiation. Schrodinger was later able to show the equivalence of his wave-mechanical treatment of the problem of atomic radiation and the methods of matrix mechanics developed by Heisenberg, Born and Jordan. He succeeded Max Planck as professor at Berlin in 1927 but in 1940 he left Germany and joined the Institute of Advanced Studies in Dublin. In 1956 he retired to Vienna.

THOMSON, George Paget (1892–), the only son of J. J. Thomson, was born at Cambridge on 3 May; he was educated at the Perse School and Trinity College, Cambridge. He served in France in the 1914–18 war and in 1922 became professor of physics at Aberdeen. While there he demonstrated the diffraction of electrons for which he was, jointly with C. J. Davisson, awarded the Nobel prize in 1932. From 1930 to 1952 he was head of the physics department of the Imperial College of Science and Technology in London, where he worked on atomic energy, especially on attempts at controlled thermonuclear fusion. He became a fellow of the Royal Society in 1930, was knighted in 1943, and was Master of Corpus Christi College, Cambridge, from 1953 to 1962.

THOMSON, John Joseph (1856–1940), the discoverer of the electron, was born on 18 December at Cheetham Hill, Manchester. At the age of fourteen he entered Owens College, Manchester, from which he went in 1876 to Trinity College, Cambridge, as a minor scholar, and remained there in one capacity or another for sixty-four years. He won the Adams prize in 1883 for an essay on vortex rings as a possible feature of atomic architecture, and in 1884 he became a fellow of the Royal Society and succeeded Rayleigh as Cavendish professor, a position he held until his retirement in 1919. At Princeton, New Jersey, U.S.A., in 1896 he gave four lectures in which he speculated on atomic structure, and the next year on 30 April at a Friday evening discourse at the Royal Institution he announced his discovery of the electron. During the next seven years he investigated its properties and behaviour and also laid the foundations of mass-spectroscopy, later to be so ably developed in his laboratory by Aston. In 1906 Thomson was awarded the Nobel prize and he received the Order of Merit in 1912. He was President of the Royal Society from 1915 to 1920 and Master of Trinity College from 1919 until his death. His ashes were buried in Westminster Abbey. It was J. J. Thomson's influence and inspiration which made the Cavendish laboratory the centre of modern physics that it became during the first quarter of the twentieth century.

VOLTA, Alessandro, Count (1745–1827), was born on 18 February at Como, Italy, the son of wealthy parents. He was educated at the Jesuit college there until he was sixteen years old, and thereafter he continued his studies privately. In 1769 he published a paper describing electrical phenomena, and in 1774 he became professor at Como; the year following he published an account of his invention of the electrophorous, a simple electrostatic machine for generating electricity by induction. This brought him fame and in 1779 he was elected to the newly founded chair of experimental physics at Pavia which he occupied until his retirement forty years later. He travelled abroad, and in 1791 was made a fellow of the Royal Society of London; in 1810 Napoleon made him a Count and in 1815 the Emperor of Austria appointed him to be director of the philosophical faculty of the university of Padua. Volta was fascinated by Galvani's discovery of electrical stimulation of a frog's muscle; his researches enabled him to explain the phenomenon and led him to invent the electric pile which provided the first source of a continuous current of electricity – a source which Faraday used in his early experiments on electrolysis. Volta's discoveries were of such consequence that the unit of electrical potential is named after him.

WHEWELL, William (1794–1866), was born in Lancaster on 24 May. He entered Trinity College, Cambridge, as an exhibitioner, he was senior wrangler in 1816 and when he was twenty-six years old was elected a fellow of the Royal Society. He became professor of mineralogy in Cambridge in 1828, but resigned after four years; from 1838 to 1855 he was professor of moral theology and casuistical divinity. He was made Master of Trinity College in 1841 and Vice-Chancellor of the University in 1842. He was the author of many philosophical, mathematical and scientific works, but his most influential writing was published in 1858. This was *Novum Organum Renovatum* in which he set forth a nineteenth-century revision of scientific method that had been initiated by *To Organon* of Aristotle and developed in the *Novum Organum* of Francis Bacon.

YOUNG, Thomas (1773–1829), was born at Milverton, Somerset, on 13 June to a Quaker family and was the youngest of ten children. He was said to have been able to read at the age of two, and by the time he was fourteen years old he was acquainted with Latin, Greek, French, Italian, Hebrew, Persian and Arabic. In 1792 he started the study of medicine in London but transferred to Edinburgh after two years and then to Göttingen in 1795. Having obtained his medical degree he went to study at Emmanuel College, Cambridge, for a couple of years before setting up in practice in London. He was appointed to a professorship at the Royal Institution in 1801 but he relinquished it two years later fearing that it would interfere with his medical practice. His interests were at first physiological; in 1793 he described the mechanism of accommodation by which the curvatures of the surfaces of the crystalline lens are altered to enable the eye to focus on both near and distant objects; in 1801 he explained the defect of vision known now as astigmatism. In this year too he published his greatest scientific discovery, the interference of light waves; during the next quarter of a century this inspired the work of the great French mathematical opticians Fresnel and Arago and the German Fraunhofer. Young's name is associated with the modulus of elasticity, but more especially with the three-colour theory of vision later advocated by Helmholtz, and brought into prominence again today by recent biochemical researches on the pigmentation of the retinal cones. The modern concept of energy may also be said to have originated with Young. He was not only physician, optician, physicist and mathematician but also a connoisseur of music, an artist and a skilled horseman, and for his contributions to Egyptology alone is he worthy of remembrance. The triply inscribed stone found at Rosetta in 1799 proved to be the key to understanding of Egyptian records, and by 1814 Young had translated the demotic text and a few years later had made considerable progress in deciphering the hieroglyphs. He was nimble minded and interested in everything – even insurance and navigation!

YUKAWA, Hideki (1907–), was born on 23 January. He studied at the University of Kyoto in Japan where in 1939 he became professor of physics after having served for three years as professor at the University of Osaka. In 1935 he suggested the meson theory of nuclear forces; for this he was given the Nobel prize for 1949, mesons having in the meantime been detected by C. D. Anderson. In 1948 Yukawa visited America, spending a year at the Institute for Advanced Study at Princeton, N.J., and two years at Columbia University, New York City. He returned to Japan to be director of the Research Institute for Fundamental Physics at Kyoto.

INDEX

107

109